CW00550289

Pit Ponies

Pit Ponies

John Bright

B.T. Batsford Ltd, London

Dedicated to the memory of my friend, the late Fred Law, farmer, horsedealer and raconteur extraordinary, whose reminiscences, so colourfully told, sowed the seed of this book.

First published 1986

ISBN 0 7134 52269
Typset by
SB Datagraphics
Colchester, Essex
and printed in Great Britain by
Anchor Brendon
Tiptree, Essex
for the publishers
B.T. Batsford Ltd.
4 Fitzhardinge Street
London W1H 0AH

Frontispiece: A pit pony and miner at Lady Windsor Colliery.

Contents

Acknowledgements

Above all others I am indebted to the very many miners, ex-miners, vets, colliery officials and other individuals who, in letters and in conversation, provided so much of the subject matter of this book. My thanks are also due to Eric Bower and Hugh Geddes for help with the illustrations, to Clive Crickmer of *The Daily Mirror* and the Editor of *Coal News* for invaluable publicity at the outset of the project, and to Bob Murrie for advice on the technical aspects of mining. The National Coal Board helped in a wide variety of ways, and Margaret Norwell, Librarian of the North of England Institute of Mining and Mechanical Engineers, always gave her valuable assistance readily and kindly. My wife Pam provided secretarial assistance at the busiest times and I am particularly grateful for the support and encouragement that she and my daughters Fiona and Lyn lavished on me throughout.

J.W.B.

The author and publisher would like to thank the following for permission to reproduce the illustrations:
Beamish North of England Open-air Museum, Nos. 3, 4, 6, 7, 14, 18, 24, 28, 31, 32, 35; T. Brennan and the County Archivist of Durham (Durham Records Office D/Ph 83/80) No. 44; Mrs Churm and the County Archivist of Durham (Durham Records Office D/MRP 84/30) No. 48; D. Davis, No. 22; C. Doorbar, No. 36; H. Geddes, No. 52; J. Hodgson, Nos. 49, 50, 51; G.A. Jolley, No. 43; W. Law, 16, 17, 45, 47; The National Coal Board, Hobart House, Nos. 15, 29, 39, 53, 57, 58; The National Coal Board, North East Area, Nos. 5, 21, 40; The National Museum of Wales, Nos. 34, 42, 46; The Newcastle Chronicle and Journal Ltd, Nos. 9, 30; The North of England Institute of Mining and Mechanical Engineers, Nos. 8, 10, 11, 12, 13, 19, 25, 26, 27, 33, 37; Wally Talbot Photography and Daniel Thwaites and Co. Ltd, No. 2; B. Walker and the Newstead Branch of the NUM, No. 56; the late Owen Watson, Nos. 20, 38; Mrs Owen Watson and Scollins and Titford Ltd, Nos. 1, 41; John Cornwell for the cover photograph, frontispiece and Nos. 23, 54.

1 Workmate.

Notes

1 As most of this book refers to the period before decimal coinage was introduced to Britain, sums of money quoted are in pounds, shillings and pence. There were 12 pence in a shilling, and twenty shillings in a pound. For example, £15.10/- (or £15.10s.0d) represents fifteen pounds, ten shillings and no pence, equivalent to £15.50 in decimal currency.

2 Horses are measured in 'hands', their height being taken at the withers, in front of the saddle where the neck begins. A hand is 4 inches (approx. 10.2cms.) and the height is normally expressed as the number of hands and the number of inches left over. For example, a pony 50 inches high is described as 12 hands, 2 inches, or 12.2 h.h. (hands high). In conversation this would probably be abbreviated to 'Twelve two'.

2 Acknowledgement of a long partnership – the mineworkers' representative Joe (now Lord) Gormley toasts the pit ponies' representative at the opening of *The Pit Pony* public house at Ashton-in-Makerfield in April, 1979.

Preface

The slightly unusual style of this book needs some explanation.

The death, some years ago, of an acquaintance of mine from whom I had heard many fascinating 'horsey' stories, made me very aware of the imminent passing of the last generation who actually worked with horses – worked seriously, that is, ploughing and leading and coal-mining and so on. So I set out to collect tales of the experiences of these old horse-men, before it was too late and, as I lived in a colliery area, I found that many of the yarns were about pit ponies. Never having worked in a mine my knowledge of the facts of the pit ponies' lives was not very great, so I tried to find out more about them, only to discover that there was no standard source of information. It was then that I decided to try to tell the story of the pit ponies, whenever possible letting the men who had actually worked with the animals do the telling for me.

A little publicity in the press – the *Daily Mirror* and *Coal News* were particularly helpful – and on T.V. and radio, and the contributions came flooding in; hundreds of letters, telephone calls, invitations to visit and talk about the ponies ... Many, many, miners and ex-miners also felt that the horses that worked underground needed their story telling, and were eager to help. All the detail I needed, it seemed, the old mining horse-men would supply.

Hence the style that you will find on the following pages: facts and observations about pit ponies, drawn from, illustrated and exemplified by the personal experiences of the men with first-hand knowledge. Wherever possible I have quoted the miners' exact words, though whilst giving a ring of authenticity to the points being made, this creates a few difficulties of its own. For example, the miners quoted live in all parts of the country, and conditions, techniques and vocabulary differ considerably from coalfield to coalfield, even from pit to pit. Moreover, all the views offered by miners are of course subjective and therefore more or less prejudiced, and the reader needs to bear this in mind.

This book is not intended in any way to pretend that it is a definitive study of the lives and work of horses underground. So what is it? The very best way, now, I believe, for a person to find out what it was really like for pit ponies down a mine would be to collect together a group of ex-drivers, horsekeepers and vets from different coalfields, with someone interested to keep order, and then for the person to listen to them, question them, and let them tell their stories. Gradually a living picture of men and horses working together underground would emerge ...

This book is intended as a substitute for that discussion.

J.W.B.

1 The Horse and the Coal-Mining Industry

Horses have been associated in different ways with coal-mining ever since coal was first extracted from the earth in commercially viable quantities. The history of their contribution both above and below ground charts many advances in the technology of mining and reflects the changes in attitudes both of those people closely associated with the winning of coal and the nation as a whole. When the pits were literally nothing more than pits or holes in the ground horses were used for transporting the coal away from them. As the pits were sunk deeper horses were used to power the 'gins' and windlasses by which the coal was raised from seam-level to the surface. As the demand for coal grew and its importance to industry and the national economy increased, so mining knowledge and technology advanced and the working coal-faces moved further out from the pit-shafts. Then horses, so much stronger than humans, were taken down the mine itself to provide the power for haulage which had previously been supplied by men, women and children. From that time for more than two hundred years the task of moving the coal from the coal-face along the narrow passages to the main tunnels, a process known as 'putting' in the north, 'ganging' in the midlands and 'driving' or 'hauling' in other coal-fields, was done mainly by ponies. Larger horses would then lead the coal to the shaft-bottom, or, on the advent of early forms of mechanical haulage on the 'main roads', to the furthest extent of that system. All these animals working underground were referred to collectively as 'pit ponies', but in fact their work would further define them as 'putting ponies', 'stint ponies', 'driving horses', etc. When further increase in industry's demand for coal led to the invention of machines which could cut the coal faster than the ponies could transport it, the phasing out of the pit ponies began. Further developments in mechanical haulage underground accelerated the process until, by the 1970s, very few ponies were left.

The presence of the ponies underground, throughout their history, has always been at least a matter to be commented on and frequently a subject of great debate and controversy, for pit ponies are regarded in very different ways by different people. Management, the animal-lovers among the general public and the underground workers all see the ponies from a different standpoint.

Management and coal-owners have tended to see the pony only as a crucial link in the process of bringing coal from the seam to the customer: a unit, therefore, in the economics of coal production. The management's concern for the pony thus centred upon the obtaining of maximum labour from minimum outlay. The ponies represented capital investment and their care and upkeep were expenses contributing to the cost of winning the coal, and so influenced profits. This economic interest of the management in the pit ponies may be seen as the single most influential element in the life and work of the horses underground, for upon it depends every aspect of the care and conditions of work experienced by the ponies during the days of the private ownership of the mines. In its most extreme form it is well illustrated by the following apocryphal tale, in which a pony had been killed and the driver had to face the manager. 'How did this happen?' asked the manager. 'Well, sir,' stuttered the awe-struck driver-lad, 'I couldn't get to the ventilation door in time. If I hadn't got out of the way and saved myself, *I* would have been killed.' 'No doubt,' said the manager, 'but we have to buy ponies.'

The general public, on the other hand, has always disregarded the economic aspects of the pit pony, seldom even making any connection between the ponies and the price of the coal that householders bought. Instead, the animal-loving public has tended to be aware only of the shameful inhumanity practised when, as they see it, a noble and beautiful animal, evolved to survive by fleetness of foot on the plains, is forced into dangerous and arduous slave labour underground in the dark. Societies and branches of societies have been formed to protect the interests of pit ponies, influencing politicians to legislate in their favour and forcing from the coal industry frequent protestations concerning the care and consideration lavished upon the animals.

The man in the middle, between the two extremes of cost-conscious management and protective public, was the miner. To the pitman the pony was an involuntary workmate and was treated as such, with all that implies. The pony driver had no control over, and usually no knowledge of, the financial management of the pony he drove; neither could he stand back and take the detached and idealistic view of the public. He worked with the pony; together they were a success or a failure as a working team, experiencing the same conditions, exposed to the same dangers and providing for each other what respite and companionship there was to be found.

The working conditions varied from pit to pit. Not until the formation of the National Coal Board in 1947 was there much consistency in the treatment of ponies or men. There were good mines and poor mines, by whatever criteria they were judged. Conditions were determined by a number of factors – the geological formations round the coal seams, the thickness of the seams themselves, the temperature, the water present, the gas potential. All of these made the work more or less difficult, disagreeable and dangerous, but the organisation of the labour at a particular pit, and the management's attitudes, also exerted considerable influence on the nature of the toil of man and beast alike. Pressures exerted by the owners passed down through the hierachy of the mine until they settled on the shoulders of the labour force, and through the miners the ponies received their share of the stress. Society wanted coal and wanted it cheap. The shareholders wanted their profits. Management was therefore under pressure to produce the coal and to produce it efficiently and economically. The miners, to take home a living wage, had to move a maximum of coal in the minimum of time, so they worked hard and fast and the ponies, without the financial motivation of the men, had to be made to work hard and fast.

The ponies were often grossly overworked, but the critical nature of their contribution to the task of bringing the coal to the surface could not pass unnoticed. The importance of the work was such that it made sense to ensure that the ponies were in a state of health and fitness which would enable them to do it to the best of their ability. A sick, sorry or underfed pony obviously would not work as well as one that was kept in good condition and looked after. Considerations of humanitarian treatment need not come into it, for it made good sense economically. As early as 1857 Fordyce, describing a visit to Wearmouth Colliery in his *History of Durham*, was able to comment:

Now you can see the remarkable smoothness of the horses' coats and the sleekness of the ponies' appearance. The horses get fat, the men lean; the ponies well-conditioned and the lads ill-conditioned.

Fit and contented animals would work better and last longer. Men didn't have to be bought.

Well-conditioned pit ponies were exhibited in appropriate classes at agricultural shows and horses of great age could be displayed at most collieries as examples of contented lives, for, surely, it could be argued, a horse totally at odds

3 Deputy watching a boy hand-putting a tub. Mickley Colliery, about 1920.

with its working surroundings, and negligently cared for in its stable will not last, in good health and apparently in good spirits, well into old age? As a member of the Institute of Mining Engineers wrote in 1902:

On the writer's desk is a polished hoof, the silver-mounted inscription of which reads as follows: SWALLOW. A 10 hands Shetland pony, was 5 years old when put to work down Kimblesworth Pit on 2 May 1876. He ceased work 22½ years later on 12 October 1898, aged 27 years. During the whole of his working life he never had a sick or sorry day, the 6 weeks strike of 1879 and the 13 weeks strike of 1892 being the only occasions on which he was idle. On 8 August 1896, when 25 years old, he took 3rd. prize among 20 other pit ponies shown in Durham.

Yet, despite such illustrations, there was still, in the minds of animal-loving men and women in the street, a sincere and strong misgiving that it was morally wrong to deprive a living creature of its rightful inheritance of natural life, which, for a horse, should include fresh air, grass and sunlight, and that no amount of care and attention could ever right that wrong.

There were miners who thought the same way too, and the paradox of the kindnesses rendered to the pony workmate within a context of the possible cruelty in keeping the pony underground at all, disturbed many a driver. As one miner commented:

Of all the cruelties that have been committed against the animal world, surely the sending of ponies underground to haul must be the worst. Having said that, I must selfishly admit that those marvellous little creatures gave me the happiest moments of the 16½ years I worked in the pit.

Other pitmen, though, confess never to have thought about it, simply taking the presence of the pit pony in the mine for granted. No miner could afford to be sentimental, for while the coal had to be moved from face to surface, the power

4 Memorial postcard sold to benefit victims of the West Stanley disaster in February 1909. William Gardner risked his life to save the pony pictured here and 'Paddy' was presented to him by the owner of the pit.

had to come from somewhere, and in the days before machinery if it was not provided by horses it was provided by men, or even by women and girls and boys. Even some miners retiring in the 1960s could recall doing underground haulage by the strength of their own muscles: '*We had two pits which did not have ponies. I worked in one at 17 years of age, and did the putting in atrocious conditions for three shillings a shift.*' Bringing ponies into mines which had previously been without them '*eased the putter's life, as even pushing the empty tubs from the siding to the face we boys used to need the men to come and help us. So it was a big help to have a pony to steady the full tubs out.*'

The relationship between the driver and his pony is a complex one; the man and the animal brought together to carry out an unpleasant and arduous task in dark and dangerous conditions, the man compelled by the system under which he operated to force the animal to work extremely hard, yet aware that the pony and he suffered very similar privations. The occasion was there for the animal to be taken advantage of, and willing horses were taken advantage of, pulling the extra tub, working the double shift. The opportunity was there for the driver, roughly handled by the men he served, to handle the pony roughly in turn, and there were drivers happy enough to take the opportunity. Some drivers were quick-tempered, some were bullies, others simply unintelligent or unthinking, and in some pits and at some times ponies undoubtedly suffered at the hands of such workers, to such an extent that miners who only ever worked in that one colliery could well believe that descriptions of any other kind of behaviour could only be fanciful. As one such miner wrote:

Pit ponies in general were badly treated in maybe 90 cases out of a hundred. The devotion of a man for his pony is a fallacy. I couldn't recall the number of times I have seen a pony flogged, kicked, punched and even subjected to worse cruelty. The more awkward the pony, the more vicious the punishment meted out. Young men were on piece work, and depended on the pony. Complaints of the ill-treatment were rare, and the management didn't want to hear them.

Moreover, as the men varied, so did the ponies. Some were slow to learn or insufficiently trained, some were of a stubborn nature, some were mean and almost unmanageable, and horses of these kinds were always likely to create frustration in a man relying upon their assistance to earn his daily bread, and all too often the frustration did break out in violent treatment of the ponies.

There was, though, another side to the treatment question: one in which the ponies could be seen as *'magnificent animals, our staunch companions, which, even in the bad old days were loved and well-looked-after'*. The interdependence of man and beast and the shared adversity could also result in a comradeship and trust that fostered only the kindest of behaviour and the fondest of care. The importance of the horse as companion should not be underestimated, for many of the drivers were young lads perhaps only fourteen years old, often converted from schoolboy to underground worker literally overnight; they would travel in the dark and narrow roadways with no company but the pony for much of each shift and it is small wonder that many of these lads, bewildered and frightened as many of them confess to being, developed a great affection for their pony workmate. Many made a habit of taking in treats for their pony each day, fruit, vegetables, bread, even sweets, and in the tough male world of the mines such expressions of affection say a great deal. So, too, do the stories, so common in mining communities, in which the life of a man is saved by the 'sixth sense' of his pony, or where a miner risks his own life to save his horse. They speak of a bond which somehow raised the relationship of the miner and the pit pony above the harsh economic realities of the circumstances which brought them together and although there certainly were pits where cruelty abounded, the companionship of one living creature with another did, in the main, make working underground a little less hard to bear.

The phasing out of the ponies from the pits is an operation which highlights the dual nature of the miner's regard for his pony. Whilst being glad for the animals' sake that they were being released, he could not help but recognise that the mines would be a poorer place for their going: '*Whilst I agree that it is a great step forward when the ponies went out of the mines, I must admit that a lot of character went out of the pits when they left.*' Or, as another miner put it, *'Machines get the work done faster, but I don't fancy sharing my sandwiches with a diesel locomotive.'* It is this notion of sharing which is the essence of the relationship and which remains strongest in the minds of many miners who worked as pony-drivers at the outset of their careers underground. Shared sandwiches, shared labour, shared danger, even shared attitudes:

When you'd go to work in the morning, there'd be a string of them, going up the underground road; they'd be walking as if they didn't care whether they went or not. But coming back, at the end of the shift, they'd be at full gallop if you didn't stop 'em.

A glib response, when the subject of common conditions for miners and ponies is raised, is that the important distinction is that the ponies had no choice whether they went down the mine, whilst the miners were free agents to work elsewhere if they wished. In theory this is obviously so, but the reality of life in the mining communities in the nineteenth and early twentieth centuries was different. The vast majority of miners had no more choice than the ponies had; mining was traditionally a father-to-son occupation, occasioned both by the necessity for the youngest to become a breadwinner as soon as possible and by the expectancy of the management of a mine that their workers' sons would

5 Workmates and companions. *Above:* the driver attaches the shaft-iron to connect pony to tubs.
6 *Below:* a 'bait-stand' or food-break, and the pony is as interested in the boy's 'bait' as in the contents of his 'choppy-box'.

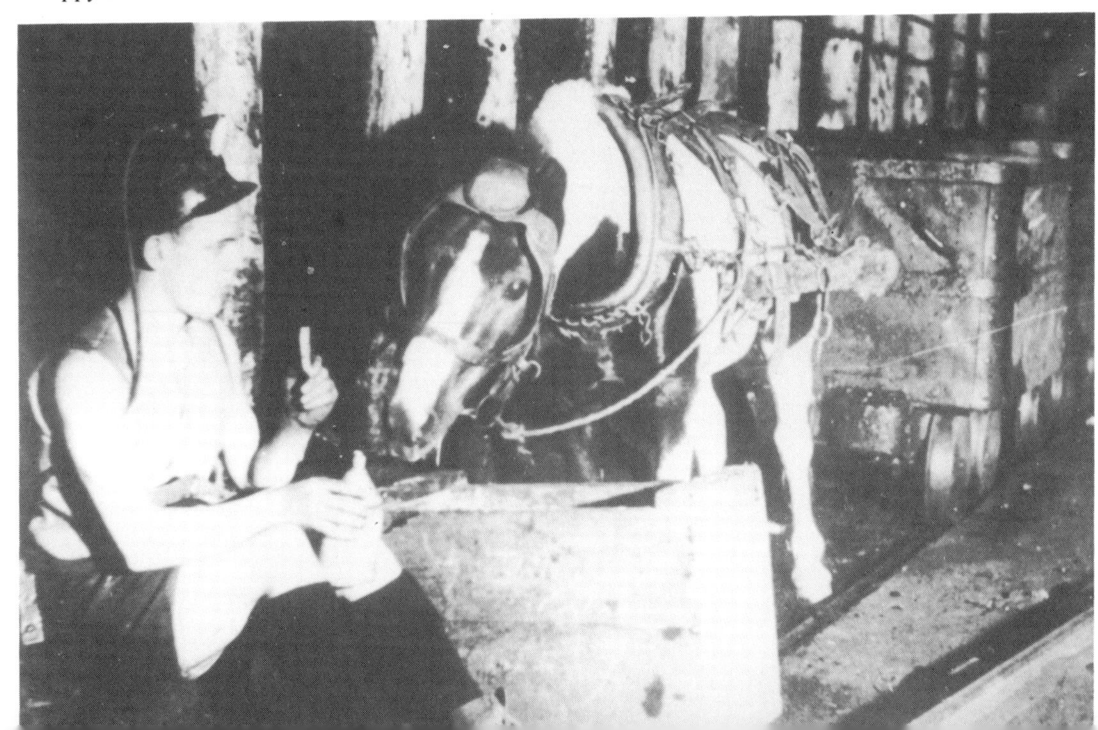

7 The team; boy and pony in normal working environment, except that light has been provided for the photographer where there would usually be complete darkness.

also take up employment there – an expectancy which might be backed up by threats of losses of job and house for father if they didn't – and by the simple facts that there was no other employment available in the locality and the family had no money to spare for further education. Indeed, it is possible that a miner's bitter awareness that society *was* treating him no differently from the pony he drove might be an important link in the chain that bound many of these working pairs together.

It will be seen in the following chapters, particularly those which deal with a specific aspect of the pit ponies' work in the mines, that the concept of a man and pony as a pair or team is a fundamental one. Only occasionally is it possible to discuss the pony without any reference at all to his driver, and even then the influence is still clearly discernible.

2 A Brief History of the Pit Ponies

The three phases of coal transportation – underground haulage, raising to the surface and above-ground haulage – have all been conducted entirely by horse-power at some period in the history of the coal-mines. First of all, horses were used simply to move the coal from the pits to wherever in the locality it was needed, or, as the trade grew, to the nearest boats, for the roads of sixteenth century England were not conducive to the long-distance haulage of heavy loads. So bad were the roads, so rutted in summer, so muddy in winter, that carts could not be used even for relatively short deliveries and pack animals carrying the coal in panniers, baskets or bags, had to be employed. Obviously such a system was suitable only for small amounts and economically viable only over short distances. As the trade increased improvements in transport were desperately needed and as early as the reign of Queen Elizabeth I experimental wooden wagonways were being laid. The first seems to have been in Nottinghamshire where, in 1597, Huntingdon Beaumont built a two-mile track of 4″ square wooden rails, resting on sleepers, to the River Trent at Wollaton. By 1608 there were three wooden wagonways in the north of England. The rails made an impressive increase in the amount of coal that could be moved at one time. Even with 17th century engineering the mining concerns could obtain '*bulky carts with four rollers fitting these rails, whereby the carriage is so easy that one horse will draw 4 or 5 chaldrons of coal*'.

The 'chaldron' became standardised later at 53 cwts, so the horse was pulling 10 or more tons of coal – which, elsewhere, it was stated to be capable of moving 24 miles in one day – a much greater load than it could possibly carry in panniers.

The rails were first made of cheap timber such as fir or birch, then later this was improved by the addition of a beech top. Not until 1716 is there any evidence of metal being used and then only as a harder-wearing strip of cast iron on top of the wood. Improvements were taking place, though, as far as the vehicles and the rail systems were concerned. In 1698 Sir Humphrey Waller was writing about the experiments being made in the use of sailing techniques in the land transport of coal, in '*new sailing wagons for the cheap carriage of his coal to the waterside, whereby one horse does the work of ten at all times, but when any wind is stirring one man and a small sail does the work of twenty*'. The sailing wagon, despite the claims, was not developed but in the early 18th century a significant improvement did gain general acceptance. This was 'Inclined Plane Surface Haulage', developed particularly in the mining areas on Tyneside, which were geographically particularly well suited to it. In this system a wagonway was built which made use of the contours of the land and the slopes down towards the river, so that the whole wagonway was, as far as possible, on one inclined plane. Loaded wagons would then run from the pit-head to the loading staithes by gravity and horses were only required to pull the empty wagons back uphill to the mine. At the outset of Inclined Plane Haulages the horses walked behind the wagons on the downward trip, but '*a subsequent improvement was the provision of a low carriage attached to the rear of the train, in which the horse was conveyed down*' – an arrangement which the horses are stated to have become

accustomed to very soon *'and to have been fond of'*.

By the late 1600s horses were also being used to raise the coal from the working levels in the pits to the surface by means of cog-and-rung gins, machinery which translated the horizontal power of the horses walking round and round to the vertical plane of a winding mechanism which lifted the containers of coal up the pit shaft. A lawsuit of 1667 refers to a rent for 'coal wrought' and the defendant was to find sufficient horses and drivers for 'drawing the coals to bank'. *The Compleat Collier* of 1718 states that a pit 60 fathoms deep on a good day will mine approximately 90 tons and that *'such a pit will require, at least, 8 horses every day to perform that work, which is always customary; four shifts of horses, two at a time, and, indeed, you should have a spare shift, or two more horses ready'*. In 1680 a 40 fathom pit in Northumbria was also requiring 8 horses to work a cog-and-rung gin to raise 90 tons a day.

The opening decades of the 19th century saw

8 Inclined plane haulage on wooden rails. A coal wagon and the staithes at Newcastle are pictured in *L'Art d'exploiter les Mines de Charbon de Terre* by M. Morand, 1773.

rapid changes in the above-ground transportation of coal for two major reasons. One was the shortage of horses and fodder for them brought about by the demands of the war against Napoleon, and the other was the advent of steam power. The requisition of horses for military service and the rise in price of both animals and food for them meant that coal-owners looked urgently for alternative sources of motive power. Christopher Blackett, of Wylam in Northumberland, looked back in history and tried to use oxen, but the main hope lay in the new miracle of steam engines. The progress of the invention is well known and it is sufficient here to record that the beginning of the end for horses on railways above ground was signalled by Blenkinsop's locomotive working from Middleton Colliery to Leeds in 1812 and that by 1880 there were no horse-drawn railways left in

9 A replica of an eighteenth century wooden coal wagon on wooden rails on the original track bed at Causey Arch in County Durham, 1983. The wagon held 53 cwts. of coal.

operation. Similarly, steam took over the work of powering the winding gear to raise the coal and, except for the movement of wagons round the yards and local deliveries of coal along the improving roads, the horse became redundant at the pithead.

Underground, the business of moving the coal from the workings to the pit or shaft where it could be raised to the surface, had been carried out manually from the time that the miners had begun to work in a horizontal direction along the seams, away from the pit sides. The coal was simply placed in a container of some kind and then carried or dragged to the shaft. Until Lord Ashley's parliamentary bill of 1843 forbade it, this work was often done by women and children, particularly, according to Fordyce, in Scotland, where the unfortunate female and child labourers in this 'bearing system' carried the coals on their backs in wicker creels or baskets. The first improvement on the bearing system was the introduction of the wooden sledge. The coal was put into large baskets or 'corves', which were dragged along on the sledges by one or two persons who were called 'coal-putters'. The sledge was succeeded by the barrow, and the barrow by a small wooden-wheeled vehicle often called a 'tram'. The underground road systems were very rough and for the trams to be used efficiently the introduction of some kind of rails underground became necessary. These various innovations were introduced at different times in the 17th and 18th centuries according to the conditions and circumstances to be found at any one mining area. However, the greatest improvement in the lot of the coal-putter was going to be one which took away from him – or her – the need to provide the muscle-power to move the sledge, barrow or tram. Exactly when the first horse was used underground for haulage is not known, but it may reasonably be presumed to be in the first half of the 18th century. The earliest reference discovered by the present writer is 1749/50, when the 14 February entry in *The Journals of John Watson*, relating to the Dyke Pit at Tanfield Moor Colliery states that '*their winnings are 8 yds. boards 3 yds. & pillars thicknefse 5 yds. & length 40 yds. Breadth of the heads abt. 1¾ yds. the height of the coal is 4ft 4ins and they put the Coal with Poney Galloways.*' The *Diary* of Edward Smith, Houghton Colliery Viewer, 1749-51, also indicates horses below ground at this time. The entry for April 1751 includes the words *'they put with horses in the West Collieries'*, and on 18 August 1750 the stocklists of items purchased in January 1750/51 by the Colliery includes *'Girthwebb, Halters, underground braughams'*. A reference to 'horsenet' may indicate the use of a strong net to lower the ponies down the shaft. In 1763 a colliery bond between Lady Windsor and John Simpson, alderman of Newcastle, owners of Harelaw, Pontop Pike, Harperly and Collierly Collieries and their workmen includes mention of *'drivers of sledge horses, drivers of gin horses'* and in 1765 Monsieur Gabriel Jars, visiting Walker Colliery, noted that horses were taken below ground and that wooden railways were also in use. Robert Galloway, in his *Annals of Coal Mining and the Coal Trade* quotes Jars as calling the vehicles running upon these rails 'charriots', and continues that *'where there were no railways made young boys used little sleds (traineaux) for drawing to the pit or horse-road'*. Certainly all the indications are that the introduction of ponies, wheeled vehicles and rails was a very irregular and haphazard affair, taken over the coalfields as a whole. Galloway, for example, also quotes from another 18th century chronicler, Brand, that *'in high seams, or strata, the coals are drawn by horses from the hewers to the shaft in sledges. In low seams, on trams, pulled by 2 small cords called soams by a boy before and pushed on at the same time by another boy behind.'* In explaining the vehicle-types further, Galloway quaintly says that a tram has four wheels *'but a sledge, properly so called, is drawn by a horse without wheels'*.

Underground wooden railways with wheeled vehicles pulled by horses became increasingly commonplace in the late 1700s as the workings extended further and further from the shafts. In 1790 efficiency was further improved by the introduction of iron rails underground in the

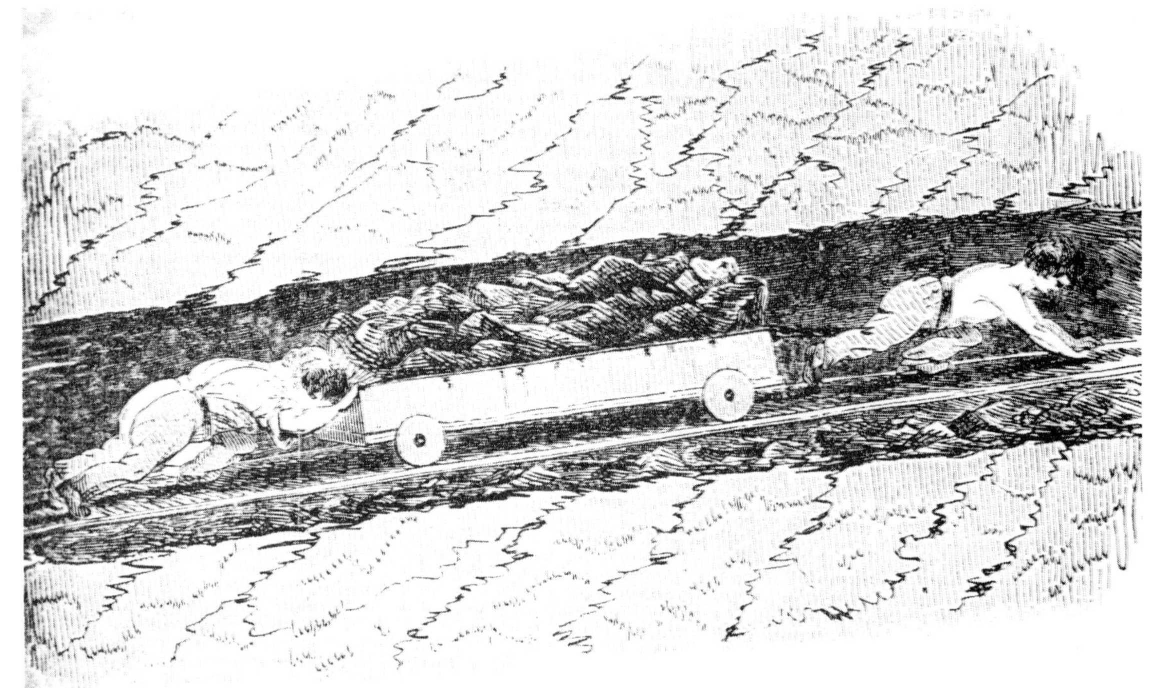

13 Pony at work in the thick coal of South Staffordshire; from the 1869 translation of L. Simonin's *Underground Life*.

main roadways, and by the mid-19th century, hastened by the changing legislation affecting boys down the mines, the putting job was increasingly taken over by small ponies. *'The change was found to be a source of economy.'* Nevertheless, in the 1970s a Derbyshire miner could still recall: *'When I first started in 1909, as a boy of 14, trammers were still being replaced by pit ponies.'*

In 1913 the population of horses underground reached 70,000, the highest recorded according to the *Government Digest of Statistics*. Even by this time, though, the importance of the horse underground had begun to decline and complete redundancy was in sight, albeit in the far future. Underground haulage engines had been installed in Hetton Colliery by 1826, and within twenty years, at Haswell and Monkwearmouth; there is also a mention of an engine drawing coal to the pit bottom at Ashby-de-la-Zouch in 1841. 'Main and Tail' Haulage was introduced to the pits round about the 1840s, a system in which the rope to pull the full train 'out-bye' to the shaft was carried 'in-bye' with the empty train. By 1892 Llanbradach Colliery had replaced all its horses by portable winches. Soon all main road or primary haulage was taken over by machinery, leaving only the putting to be done by ponies. Then, as machine-mining, first by compressed air, then by electricity around the 1930s, cut the coal ever faster, even the putting could not be done quickly enough by horse-drawn vehicles, and the conveyor-belt became universally applied to the task. So, as these inventions were implemented in the pits during the 1930s and 1940s particularly, the number of

10, 11, 12 Boys and girls drawing coal – illustrations from the Appendix to the 1st Report to Parliament of the Children's Employment Commission – Mines, Part II, 1842.

ponies in the pits declined rapidly. When the National Coal Board was formed in 1947 it acquired 21,000 pit ponies, and the Board's modernisation policies accelerated the rate of reduction. By 1962 there were 6,400 horses working below the surface; by 1967, 2,900. Five years later the number was down to 490 and by 1978 only 149 pit ponies remained.

In June 1984 the total number still at work was 55, of which 3 were employed in Wales and the rest in two North East Area pits. The 7 ponies at Sacriston Colliery in County Durham are stabled above ground and go down the shaft with the men for their shift each day, but the 45 at Ellington Colliery in Northumberland are permanently stabled underground, 'in-bye' some 3½ miles from the shaft, to cut down the time spent each day travelling to their work. Ellington is one of the most up-to-date mines in Europe, with 100% mechanisation of the coal-winning process, but with the coal being taken from seams only 300 feet below the North Sea floor it is mined by the 'pillar and bord' method which leaves certain areas inaccessible by machine-driven equipment and in such places the ponies are still the most effective and economic means of transport for salvage work and for the supply of props, girders, tools and machinery to the men. Thus, despite the NCB's intention to phase out the ponies completely by the early 1970s, these few do remain as living illustrations of the paradox of the pit pony, for the writer has visited the Ellington stables and can testify to the excellent condition of the animals and the fact that they are as well looked after as any horses above ground and far better than most, and that they do only a fraction of the workload which was expected of the putting ponies of earlier years, yet the fact remains that they are underground.

3 The Animals and Their Training

The sizes and breeds of horses and ponies employed underground depended upon the kind of work they were needed for and the circumstances in which that work had to be done. The animals ranged from very small Shetlands – a 36″ Shetland was kept for special jobs at Welbeck Colliery, for example – to 17 hands horses for main road work in the days before rope haulage was introduced. Generally ponies about 12 hands high were employed for work near the face in most coalfields, the major exception being the Northumberland/Durham area where the thinner seams meant that 10 and 11 h.h. animals were more prevalent, to the amusement and scorn of miners from other areas who felt that 'a man could pull more!' Driving and stint ponies, which worked in the higher roadways away from the coal-face, tended to be larger, with the biggest ponies, up to 14.2 h.h., being used in the Welsh and Midland pits. Collieries usually had a majority of their ponies in two sizes, for putting and driving, with one or two larger and smaller individuals for special circumstances.

Nearly all the horses used were male, very few collieries having any mares underground at all. Pit policy varied concerning the proportion of stallions and geldings. In Hartley pit, for example, in the early 1900s '*our ponies were never gelded, therefore no mares were allowed down the pit*', but a complete stable of stallions was unusual, geldings being most commonly used, alongside a few stallions. Butterley in Derbyshire did have some mares in the 1930s, but the problems are evident: '*There was talk some years previous to my going there that a mare had a foal up the roads, without anyone knowing she was pregnant. The hostler in charge got the sack.*'

The finer points of breed and breeding had little place in most underground stables. As long as the pony could do the job required of it a driver was unlikely to concern himself overmuch with the animal's forebears or origins. Most ex-pony drivers are not certain about the type of ponies they worked with: '*It is difficult to pinpoint any particular breed of pony. They were mostly of the Exmoor or New Forest type, sturdy and hardy*' or '*They were similar to Dartmoors, but on the small side.*'

The hesitancy is understandable. The collieries, when the use of pit ponies was at its height, were employing around 70,000 of them, which indicates an annual requirement of approaching 10,000 new ponies. A nation-wide trade provided these ponies from wherever the dealers could obtain them. In normal times this meant the Shetland Isles, Scotland, Wales, the Northern fells and the wild pony sales in the south-west, but in difficult periods the catchment area was extended to Iceland and Scandinavia, Russia, Belgium and even America. Thus the variety of breeds, to say nothing of the accidental and intentional crosses, to reach the coalfields, was considerable.

Some coal companies, particularly in Wales and the North East, carried out their own breeding programmes in attempts to produce the animals they wanted both in number and kind. In Wales a variety of crosses involving the Welsh Mountain Pony were carried out, to try to give the native animals shorter legs and greater strength, but the most scientific breeding programme was undoubtedly conducted in the North of England and Scotland. The evolution of the Shetland pony has been greatly influenced by the selective breeding at the Londonderry studs in the 19th century, where carefully selected Shetlands were bred to provide the Londonderry coalmines of County Durham with short but heavier animals with more bone and strength than the original island horses. On the Shetlands the ponies were used for carrying loads rather than for pulling them but they were of a size and temperament that made them an excellent substitute in the thinner-seamed pits for the boys who had, until the Children in Mines Act, pulled the tubs from the hewers at the coal-face. By 1865 more than 500 male ponies a year were being sold out of the islands, leaving the mares behind to breed more. In the early 1870s it was probably realised that the best

14 Both these horses are pit ponies! *Above:* Spider used to take the water infusion tub into South Garesfield Colliery. Being so small he could hardly manage the job, but it is said that the men were so fond of him that they used to push the tub to give him a hand.
15 *Below:* By comparison the strength and ideal working conformation of Bob from Cannock Wood Colliery, West Midlands, is plain to see.

males were being sold to work, thus weakening the breed, and a Londonderry stud was established first at Seaham Harbour in County Durham, then on the Isle of Bressay. Over the next thirty years the stud developed a new strain of Shetland pony, with a lower head carriage – a considerable advantage in the low-roofed roadways of the northern mines – and a better conformation for hauling heavy vehicles. Other coal-owners in the north-east coalfield saw the advantages both of the 'Londonderry strain' and the policy of breeding their own replacements, and many collieries in the early 1900s had small breeding units in the fields surrounding the pitheads.

There was also a marked increase in collieries rearing their own larger animals during and after the First World War when horses, because of the numbers being conscripted for war service, were in short supply and became very expensive.

The larger draught horses belowground were mainly Cleveland Bays and imported Belgian horses, both of which were used in preference to the bigger, stronger Shires because they had no 'feather' (long hair hanging over the feet). The space between the rails along which the horses walked was very often wet and dirty and the Shire's 'feathers' picked up the water and filth and the animals were prone to an unpleasant condition called 'greasy legs'.

Other imports in the early 1900s were Russian ponies and ponies from Iceland and Scandinavia. The latter were not popular with all collieries, being regarded as 'too soft', but the Russian animals were purchased in considerable numbers by companies in the North and the Midlands, and many miners recalled working with them:

A few of what we called Russian ponies (I think they were Asiatic) came into the Shipley pits. They tended to be creamy in colour, with a bristley mane, donkey-like ears and a dark line running down the back and into the tail. They were very docile and very stubborn. Where other ponies would pull a little extra when asked, these would not; no matter how much they were thrashed they would pull so much and no more. I recall on one occasion a corporal, exasperated that one of these ponies would not pull his train, hung a chain around its neck and hooked it onto a tram pulled by a more willing horse. The pony still would not budge and had to be hurriedly unhooked before his stubborn head was pulled off.

But they were not all stubborn – '*They told me Pomball was of Russian descent, very thickset and a terrific worker.*' Clifton Colliery purchased 136 Russian ponies between 1895 and 1915, but none after that.

The depression and industrial problems of the 1930s had a curious result in the pit pony trade. Unable to sell their animals, many breeders cut back on their production and in some cases were forced to dispose of part of their stock to the knackerman, with the outcome that when the situation in the coal industry improved and the demand for ponies increased there were insufficient available to satisfy the need. This led not only to ponies being imported in greater numbers from Iceland and the continent but also, for the first time, from America:

We had some shiploads from America, they used to bring fifty at a time. All little Shetlandy things, like little carthosses, ninety per cent of them coloured, and every one broken. The first lot that came over, every single pony had a leather stall-collar on, a fancy little American stall-collar, brass fittings, nice little collars with a chain under the jaw. We used to take the ponies off the boats at Liverpool – the S.S. Farmer was one.

Donkeys, too were used in considerable numbers in some areas in the late 19th century, but for some reason were not found in any quantity later on. Occasional donkeys, or asses, can be recalled by miners, but they tend to be isolated cases. Like the Shetland ponies, donkeys, where they are used for work, as in the Mediterranean countries and the Middle East, are used mainly for carrying loads on their backs and not for pulling as they do not have the strength in their hindquarters or the short, thick legs that make the good draught animal. The

16 Pit ponies from America arrive at Liverpool docks. Date uncertain; perhaps 1920s or 1930s.

numbers used in the late 1800s may have been an economy measure, as donkeys have invariably been cheaper to buy than equivalent-sized horses and have a long working life. Their decline in popularity may have been because they were found to be less efficient workers or possibly because they adapted less well to conditions underground. For whatever reason, by the time the last generation of pony drivers went into the mines, donkeys were a rarity but still existed: '*They tell too, round here, of a donkey who, working in the pit bottom, used to rush to his cornbox in a manhole when the blower went, and would not be budged from there until the end of snaptime blew.*'

The pit pony trade

By the time a pony reached a colliery it would have passed through several pairs of hands in the trade. Dealers from the coal-mining areas ranged far afield to obtain the animals to supply the local pits, buying in large numbers from the breeders, wild pony auctions and 'collector-dealers' who would assemble ponies for sale to the colliery suppliers. Various dealers are named time after time by ostlers and horsekeepers discussing the supplying of the ponies. Willy Schapiro, Maurice Morris, Srolowitz and Masarella seem to have been the last chief suppliers in the Yorkshire and Notts. and Derby coalfields, the Schapiro family being the main importers of Icelandic and Russian animals to their Doncaster yards. William Law and his son Fred, of Willington, were large-scale suppliers to the Durham mines; Barry Covitz of Glasgow was a major cog in the Shetland pony trade, and Jack Bamber of Tibshelf in Derbyshire, Jack Reep of Devon, George Rye of Skegness, Harold Shepherd of Castleford, Downey Howard of Castle Douglas, Roberts, Davies and Berry of Llanwyt and F. Evans of Llandinam were all at various times important suppliers for the mines.

Some of the account books of the Law family of Willington, County Durham, have survived and were kindly put at the disposal of the writer.

Although they form a fragmentary and incomplete record, enough remains to indicate the pattern of the pit pony trade in the North East of England from the beginning of World War I until the 1960s. There is not a great deal of detail in the individual entries, but numbers, prices, and frequently the heights are recorded. The numbers show very clearly the phasing out of the ponies – in 1947 this family supplied 905 ponies to the coal trade; by 1954 the number was down to 497; by 1960, 72; 1962, 38, and in 1963 the last 11 sales were made by the family to the NCB.

It is possible, too, from the existing books, to compile a chart of the lowest and highest prices per animal paid by the Coal Companies for bulk purchase of ponies from 1915 to 1963. It should be noted that the prices shown in the following table are the actual amounts paid and that no attempt has been made to relate the prices to the 'value of the pound' at any particular time. Nevertheless the reader should take into account the fact that, for example, a pony costing £45 in 1920 is many times more expensive than one costing a similar amount in the 1960s.

The graph on the next page shows very clearly how the prices rose to a peak during and immediately after the 1914-18 war and then slumped to a low level for ten years during the depression of the late 20s and early 30s. The trade was less affected by the 1939-45 war, but again the immediately post-war years show a marked increase in prices. An explanation can be offered for these price fluctuations if the normal effects of supply and demand are considered in the light of the fact that the pit-pony trade always had a four or five year 'time-lag'. This was brought about by two factors – the legal requirement that no horse should work underground until it was four years old, and the twelve-month gestation period in horses. Thus, though few ponies would be bred during the early years of the First World War, the main shortage would not be felt until about four years later, around 1919, just when the demand would begin to rise again, so the prices escalate. Similarly the depression saw a severe cut-back

Date	*Lowest Price*	*Highest Price*	*Date*	*Lowest Price*	*Highest Price*	*Date*	*Lowest Price*	*Highest Price*
1915	£ 8	£15.10*s.*	1931	£12.10*s.*	£15	1947	£28	£36
1916	£12	£20	1932	£10.10*s.*	£13	1948	£36	£42
1917	£15	£21	1933	£11	£13	1949	£32	£40
1918	£15	£32	1934	£12	£13	1950	£33	£36
1919	£26	£45	1935	£12	£13	1951	£33	£34
1920	£42	£45	1936	£13	£14	1952	£35	£35
1921	£42	£42	1937	£10.10*s.*	£21	1953	£36	£37
1922	£28	£28	1938	£15	£25	1954	£34	£38
1923	£16	£26	1939	£15	£20	1955	£38	£40
1924	£20	£22	1940	£15	£21	1956	£38.10*s.*	£40
1925	£18	£21	1941	£16.10*s.*	£20	1957	£38	£38.10*s.*
1926	£18	£20	1942	£16.10*s.*	£24	1958	£38.10*s.*	£40
1927	£ 8	£15	1943	£20	£23	1959	£38.10*s.*	£41
1928	£10	£15	1944	£24	£27	1960	£38.10*s.*	£41
1929	£ 7.10*s.*	£14	1945	£25	£26	1961	£38.10*s.*	£40
1930	£14	£15	1946	£27	£32	1962	£38.10*s.*	£40
						1963	£37	£44

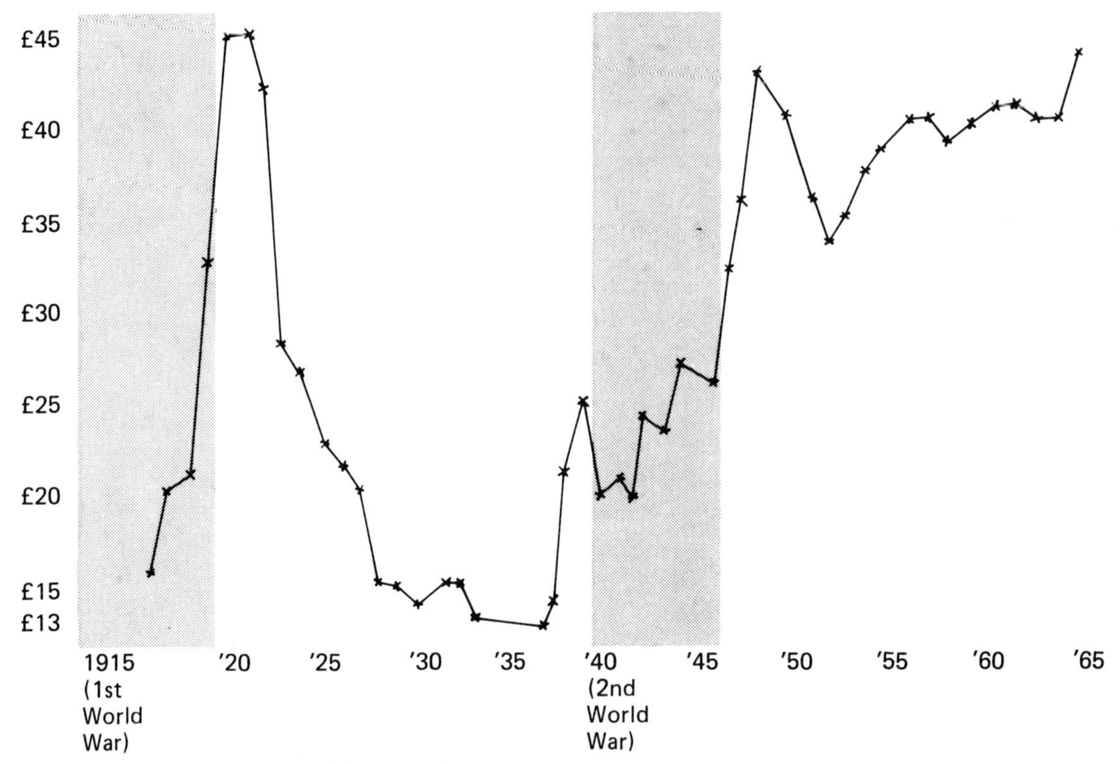

Graph of Highest Price Paid in Each Year

in breeding, so that when the coal industry began to pick up there were few ponies about for the collieries to purchase, so that prices rose and the dealers, as discussed earlier in this chapter, had to import ponies from the continent and America to satisfy the demand. Prices had just begun to stabilise five years later when the Second World War started and breeding was again halted, with a consequent rise in prices after the war. By 1950 ponies bred at the latter end of the war entered the market and prices dropped for a while only to level out and remain fairly stable for the last few years of the trade. As the ponies were phased out of the pits the breeders and dealers turned their attention to other things and the once-thriving pit pony trade quietly disappeared.

The complete 'Bought Ledger' of the Law family for the year 1947 has survived and an analysis of the purchases made that year demonstrates how wide was the catchment area of the trade to the North East coalfield. Of the 938 ponies purchased 'in bulk', 331 came from Wales, 196 from Devon, 191 from the Midlands, 190 from Scotland and 10 from Cumberland, the remaining 20 being local 'in-trade' purchases with the original sources unknown.

The ponies purchased by the Laws were normally transported by rail in cattle-wagons and unloaded at a specially constructed bay at Willington Station. From there the ponies would be herded loose through the streets to the dealer's fields just outside the town. The scene would be more like something out of the Wild West than a Durham pit village. With anything up to, and sometimes exceeding, 50 ponies, all unbroken stallions and geldings, to move through the streets, careful strategy was needed. Fred Law explained how they worked:

There were always ponies who would follow a man riding in front, so you had one rider out at the front and one at the back, and if you had a spare man you

17 Ponies destined for the pits of the North East arrive by train at Willington station. They would then be herded loose through the town's main street to the dealer's farm. This procedure continued until about 1950.

had two at the front, then one could stop up the side roads. He'd hope and pray that the openings weren't one at this side and one opposite, 'cos you could only watch one and you always used to hope that they'd go past the other! If there was an opening we used to stand, not right at the edge of the opening, but a little bit inside it, so that the ponies would start to swing in, see you and come back. Then, when the man had watched an opening, he had to go like a bat to get round in front again.

Along the town's main street there would be some assistance from spectators, though this might not be too helpful:

Sometimes the kids and the people would stand in the openings. The only fault with that was that we used to fall out with some of them because instead of just standing still they used to be shouting 'Ged up, ged up' and the ponies would be shooting off left, right and centre.

Deliveries of ponies were often undertaken the same way, herding large numbers many miles, and out in the country different tactics were sometimes used:

If you came to a bad place, like from the top of Toddles on there were little hedges and the ponies used to go through if you weren't careful, so you used to move them on a bit; you'd start to canter at the top of Toddles and canter maybe right to Binchester and keep 'em moving so they hadn't time to look for a way through.

The ponies ridden by the men learned their job too: '*I used to ride a pony that was like a sheepdog. You've seen a dog working sheep, well our ponies were nearly like that. My Mitzy used to be like that.*' In fact dogs were used to help with the herding in the dealers' fields and yards. If the ponies were already broken as, for instance, the Icelandic and Russian ponies tended to be, other methods were sometimes used:

Well, the old man used to tie, say, four across, then he would tie another four together, then he would tie the first of the second four to the tail of the inside one of the first four, so you might get three of four fours, and you're only leading one pony, but there's another fifteen with him.

The ponies would remain with the dealers until bought by the collieries. Some of the large coal companies had their own buyers who would visit the dealers and select the animals to be delivered to the different mines. Other companies sent their Chief Horsekeeper or Ostler to do the buying, others retained their Veterinary Surgeon to inspect and buy horses for them.

By law, the ponies had to be at least four years old when employed by the collieries for work underground and their age was assessed by examination of their teeth, as with horses generally. During its third year a horse replaces its second or 'middle' milk teeth by permanent ones which are long enough to be in wear when the horse is four years old. It was not unknown for dealers to purchase three-year-olds and by the removal of the middle milk teeth accelerate the process of nature so that ponies had their 'four-year-old' teeth in wear before they were actually that age. The ponies could then be sold earlier to the collieries, at greater profit, as the dealers could buy them cheaper, being younger, and did not have to feed them for so long.

Training

Ponies usually arrived at the colliery either unbroken or just trained to harness and it was up to a surface ostler or horsekeeper to prepare them for their work underground. An article in *The Colliery Guardian* in 1930 recommends that pit ponies should undergo a five-week training period on the surface, and that boys who are potential pony-drivers should attend special classes and lectures on working with ponies and caring for them. These seem merely idealistic hopes when compared with the realities of the 'training programmes' of both ponies and boys. No evidence has come to light of any such classes for pit boys anywhere in the country and the pony-training methods which have been discovered seldom approach anything like five weeks duration at the surface. The collieries wanted to know as soon as possible whether or not a pony was going to be suitable, so that if it wasn't it could be returned to the dealer to save paying for its keep any longer than necessary or so that the colliery was not short in its working pony numbers. Most training, therefore, was fairly hasty and many underground workers have complained of animals being put below ground before they were really ready for work.

The best training usually consisted of two stages: the first accustoming the pony to wearing harness and pulling heavy tubs on rails and the second getting it used to the noise and clatter of mining machinery. Some collieries included a third stage in the programme – introducing the animal to working in the dark. At many pits, though, there was little or no surface-training at all.

The first stage in most collieries usually had much in common with the training of any draught horses. The pony was introduced to the head-collar and taught to lead. If difficulties were experienced *'a centre-iron post with a swivel-attachment might be tried'* and *'wilder ponies were quietened by towing round a field at a cart-tail, pulled by a bigger horse'.* Then the rest of the harness would be added, with traces which would be attached to a log or railway sleeper to give the pony the sensation of pulling a weight. Shafts or limbers would then replace the trace harness and this could be a hazardous undertaking:

when the time came to put the shafts on the pony it had to be done very carefully, for the unaccustomed weight at the rear sometimes started them kicking, and an animal could be ruined for life if the iron end came into contact with his hocks.

An empty tub would then be hooked on and the pony led round the yards, and often the surrounding streets, until it was no longer worried by the presence and the noise of the tub behind it. Some collieries constructed a special training area for the next phase: *'My colliery had*

18 Ponies being trained to harness, using three-wheeled training tub.

a small layout of railroad made up of plates, with a few curves in the layout, and the ponies were led round, pulling empty wagons.'

At Langley Moor, near Durham *'a complete dark circuit was made, with canvas over arched girders, with canvas doors'* to simulate underground conditions. At Brancepeth Colliery, at this point in their training the ponies *'were taken to the Hutton, which was a drift mine, and we trained them there to get used to the dark'*.

These stages were often not accomplished easily, particularly with the many ponies that were quite wild and not accustomed to being handled in any way. Patience, quiet and plenty of time are considered necessary for normal horse-breaking, and though the horsekeepers may have been patient men, quietness and the freedom to take their time with their charges may often have been missing in the pit yard. Noise was to be a frequent companion of the pit ponies and they had to become accustomed to it.

A new pony, we get him used to going round on the surface then we take him to the shaft top and just let him stand there, to get used to the noise when we're winding coal, going in and out of the cage, banging and clattering. Perhaps we do this for nearly a fortnight.

The descent of new ponies into the mine was also going to be a terrifying experience for them, for however carefully the colliery might prepare them there was no way of simulating the drop down the shaft into the noisy darkness. Simonin, writing *Underground Life* in 1869, said:

The horses which draw the wagons on the underground railways are sometimes sent down into the mine fastened to a rope, but generally in the English Collieries on a properly constructed platform and cage, either in nets or baskets. When the former mode is adopted the horses do not make the slightest movement, being paralysed with fear and to all appearances dead, but when they reach the bottom of the pit they gradually recover their senses.

The 'rope' method mentioned is illustrated on p.34 with the horse being supported by a network of belts. Sometimes the sling system was used under the cage, the pony merely taking the place of the roof-bars and ropes which were

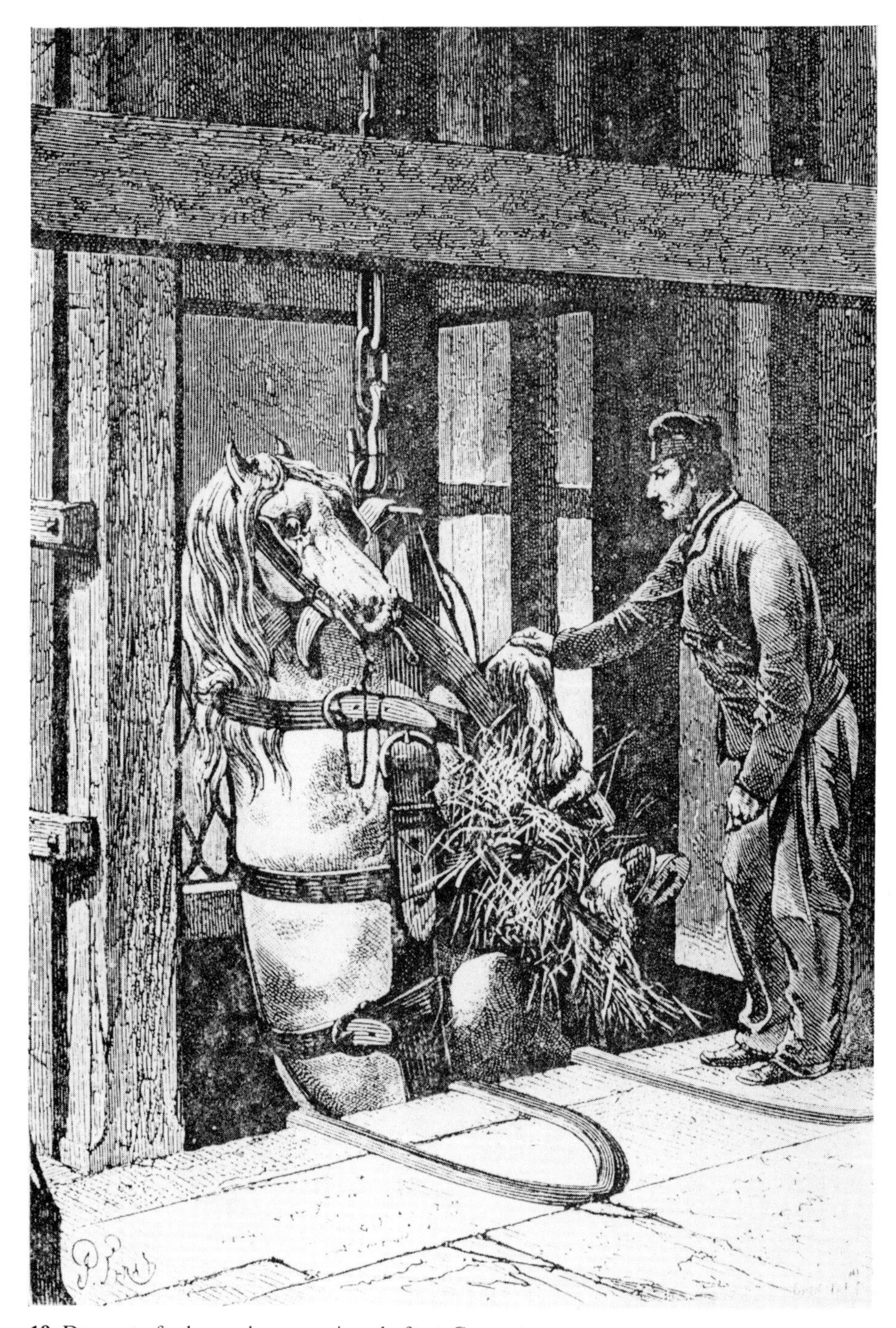

19 Descent of a horse down a mine shaft at Creuzot in France, from the 1869 translation of L. Simonin's *Underground Life*. Horses in Britain travelled up and down the shaft by similar means in the nineteenth century.

normally raised and lowered by this means, but the more usual way of transporting the ponies was by means of the cage:

We just backed them in. In the cage, where the tubs were taken out was up a height, but at ground level there were gates on there, so they used to drop the cage down to that level and back the ponies in, shut the gate, and off they went. At the other end, just lift the gates and take them out, you see.

Or, as a Leicestershire miner put it:

When the surface horse-breaker considered the trainee to be sufficiently educated he was introduced to the cage and walking around the surface machinery getting used to the bangs and crashes of productivity. A couple of days of this and the surface ostler would take a very apprehensive animal onto the cage for its first trip. The restricted area of the cage with open-design gates always proved a ticklish operation and the skill of the ostler almost like magic. Boards back and front of the pony, and just a hand-lamp for illumination. It must have been a terrible experience for the pony. The surface ostler's duties ceased when he had led, cajoled, pulled and pushed the reticent animal to the stables and handed over to the *ostler, who always worked underground.*

This operation was normally carried out at night, so that the darkness underground would not seem so strange.

Below ground the training was carried on immediately, for the horsekeeper had to find out as soon as possible whether the horse was going to be suitable for the mine. If the pony's training was successful and it entered the regular workforce it would be clipped and its mane and tail shaved or 'hogged'. If it did not take to the work or proved unfit or unmanageable then it was returned to the surface and sent back to the dealer forthwith – though the Law family account books and the Clifton Colliery horse-books indicate that only a very small percentage were in fact returned to the dealers for exchange. The mane and tail were hogged for cleanliness and practicality, and probably proved no great loss to the ponies, as there are normally no flies underground to need flicking off. The ponies were clipped in an attempt to help the ponies to counteract the very warm conditions in which they usually had to work.

The early days of training underground often proved traumatic for both the pony and its unfortunate driver. Although most collieries accustomed the ponies to harness at the surface the putting on of the shafts or 'limbers' (which in pit work are attached to the pony's harness, not the vehicle to be pulled, in the first instance) was frequently left until the animals were underground and this operation often turned out, in the cramped conditions there, to be particularly tricky:

A new pony, the first time limbers were put on, bolted and got wedged between two tubs, absolutely terrified and unable to move. Imagine the job of the putter!

It used to be hard enough getting the harness on him, but when it came to limbering him the pony almost went mad.

Some were acutely nervous, rushing, lunging in fear, often kicking resentment, but always a putter would be at the head, hanging on.

Once the pony was used to the limbers it would be time to try it out with empty tubs. Often with another pony and driver to keep it company the new recruit would be allotted to the nearest stall (hewing place) available, so that the distance it had to pull the tubs was minimal to start with.

After getting used to pulling one empty tub the load would be increased until the permitted number had been reached, according to the gradients of galleries and roadways. Now he was considered ready to be tried pulling full tubs of coal. This was usually where the fun began. Some ponies could not or would not bear onto the limmers and the 'breaker-in' had to risk being kicked or bitten. You must remember that the roadways were very narrow, so the amount of escape room was limited. It was no place for timid souls.

The pony also had to learn to 'britch' or back

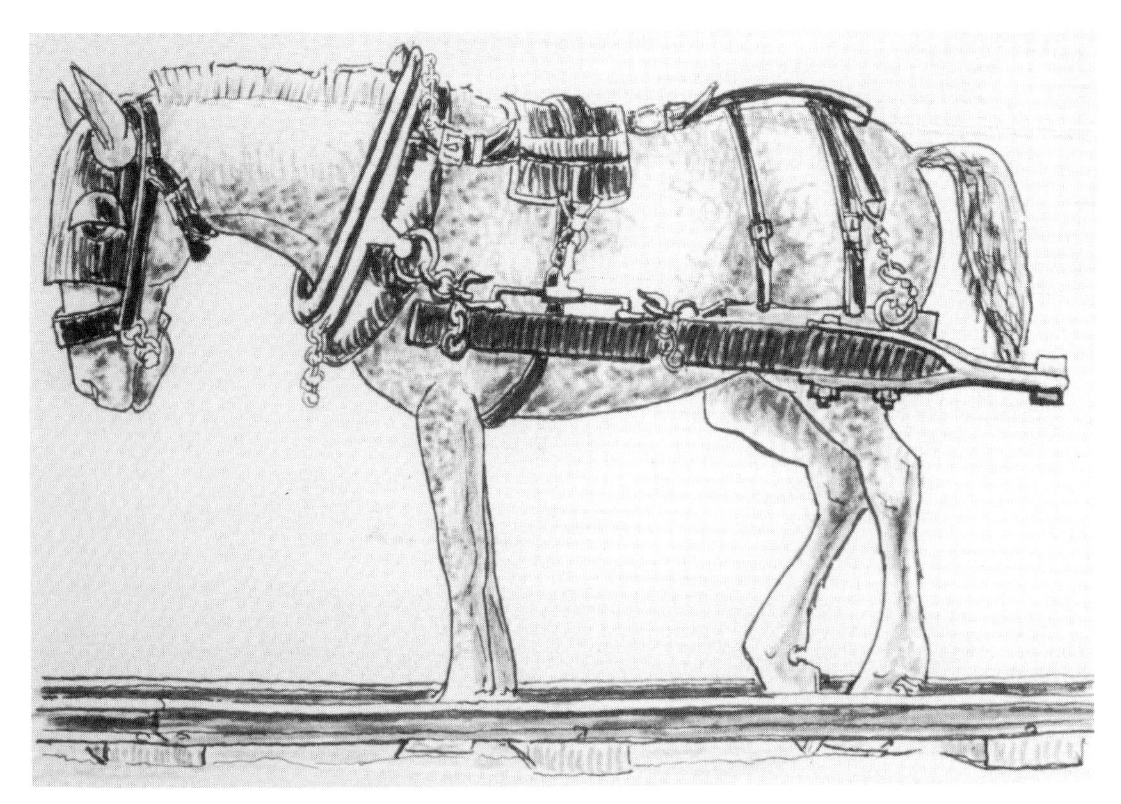

20 A pony in full limber harness. A new pit pony had more than the usual draught-horse harness to get used to; the shafts or limbers were carried all the time and fastened to each front tub in turn.

the loaded tubs, and this operation could be extremely frightening for the animal as it came into direct contact with the unseen rear harness.

There was a pony who would not britch at all, and immediately bolted when tubs ran onto his breeching strap. He galloped 300 yards out-bye, all downhill, through the haulage siding, over the brow of an incline 1 in 7, hit the side of the roadway and broke his back.

The ventilation doors in the roadways were another experience that the ponies had to learn to deal with and, by all accounts, it was a skill they soon learned.

Most ponies would open doors. The doors were made to open on the return journey from the face by pushing, and the animal soon learned to meet the door with its neck turned. A sharp flick of his head swung the door wide enough for the pony and tubs to pass through. Of course on the outward journey the driver had to pull the door open and hold it till the pony and train were through.

To start with, the ponies might try to go up the side rather than through the door, but the drivers had their own ways of dealing with this:

Part of his training included getting the pony to open ventilation doors by nosing them open. The method was to hang him on to 3 or 4 tubs on an incline, take the lockers out of the wheels and the weight of the tubs would automatically push him through the doors. Two or three goes at this and his door-opening lesson is complete. A crude way of teaching, but it certainly taught them.

As the pony learned the different parts of his job he was also being taught a variety of words of command. He would not be considered fully trained until he could perform certain tasks and operations in response to his driver's voice alone. In some pits, in Wales for example, the ponies were taught from the beginning by word of command, never ever wearing a bit, but just

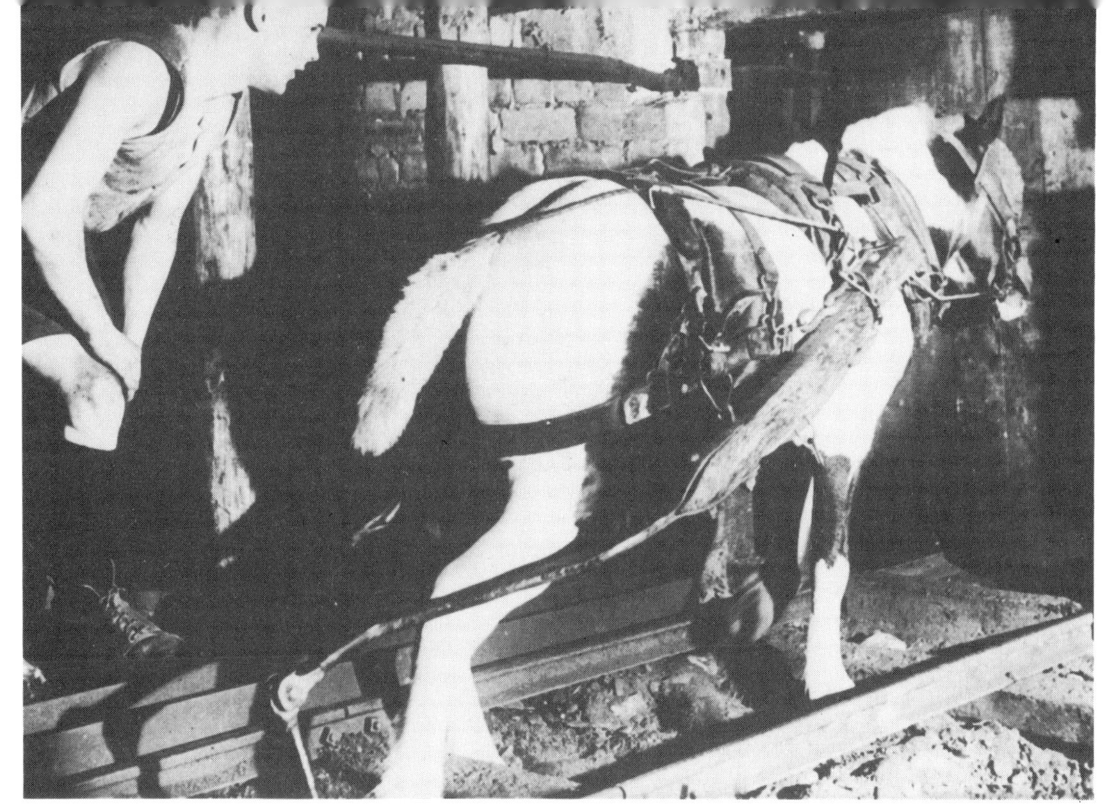

one leading-rein from the bridle on the nearside. Generally, though, the harness did include a bit and the ponies, like draught-horses above ground, were accustomed to commands accompanied by directions from long-reins by a driver behind the wagon. The commands were very often the same as the ones used for any working horses in that part of the country, but some specialist expressions were taught. In South Wales, for example, the common instructions were 'Come-me-yer' (go to the left), 'See-way' (go to the right), and 'Come-me-yer-back' (turn right round), though it must be added that, according to one Welsh miner, most horses understood both English and Welsh versions of the commands! The Derbyshire versions were 'Goo on', or Comm on' or a tongue click (to start), 'Comm agen' (when a pony reached his destination and was uncoupled from his tram 'comm agen' brought him facing in the other direction in front of his next train or flat), 'Comm back' (reversed him until he was in the right place to be coupled to his next tram), 'Ease a bit' (had the pony gently easing into his collar, a great help when the tub he was hung onto was off the track and being put back on).

21 Skills to learn; a pony noses open a ventilation door.

It can be seen from the foregoing paragraphs that, as with any other aspect of mining, the training of ponies for the pit varied enormously from mine to mine and region to region. At one end of the scale is a Midland miner's experience: '*In the 1930s, in my colliery, training was non-existent. A new pony was sent out with the driver and it was up to him to make the best of it.*' At the other end, in a Welsh colliery, '*All training was done underground. It took about twelve weeks for his basic training and he would be with that particular person for about a year, before being passed on to someone else.*' Sometimes the training was in the care of a 'horse-breaker' – '*A mis-nomer, really, just a capable putter who knew horses*' – who might be paid a shilling a day extra. The aim was an animal that would be more than merely obedient, but would do part of its work on its own, simply from habit – '*Ideally, after ponies were broken, you didn't have to give orders. You unhooked them off full tubs and they crossed the way and backed up to chummins* (*empty tubs*).'

The fear and bewilderment, though, that a pony might pass through on the way to that final, trained, state is well illustrated by the following account, told by a Yorkshire miner:

On one occasion I had been helping one of the fitters and came back to the pit-bottom to be assigned another job. The under-manager was having an argument with the horsekeeper; he looked at me and said 'You can handle a horse, can't you?' 'Yes', says I, thinking I'm in luck helping in the stables for the rest of the shift. 'Do you know your way down to the East Board?' Oh, heck, the East Board was the most hated district in the pit, all faulty strata, roof falls galore. He knew I knew the way, so he said to the horsekeeper 'Send him down with another and bring that one out.' After he had gone the horsekeeper said to me 'There's a pony down in the East Board that they can't do anything with. Take this one down and bring the other back, but watch yourself – he's only been down three days and this is his first day in the workings.' When I arrived, there stood the pony, a black with a white blaze, his neck and shoulders white with lather, sweating all over and trembling like a leaf. He still had his long mane and tail reaching to the ground. The chap in charge said 'I don't know how you're going to get him back alone, we had trouble getting him here with the other ponies.' I braided the pony's tail and tied it up in a knot so that it could not get caught up in anything and with everyone pushing and pulling we got him about fifty yards up the road and then they left me to it. I tried everything and got nowhere, till I remembered that horses that were frightened of certain stalls or shafts could be persuaded to go in blindfold, so I took off my jacket and tied it round its head and after a bit of pushing and talking to him all the way, he followed me to the pit bottom. I think he was more afraid of the shadows and the bobbing lights of the miners' lamps than anything because when I got to the pit bottom, which was well lit, I was able to take the jacket off his head and lead him without any trouble. Or did that pony sense that he was in very dangerous surroundings down the East Board? Anyway, he was deemed to be unsuitable and was sent back to the dealer.

4 Life Underground - Work

The coal-getting part of the sophisticated industry of mining is in essence quite straightforward and consists basically of three operations. The coal must first be detached from its underground seam, then transported through horizontal tunnels to the pitshaft, and finally raised to the surface. Whether one is considering the primitive methods of the 18th century miners or the complex technology of a modern colliery these basic operations are at the heart of the business.

Originally the hewing, the transporting and the lifting were all done by hand. Nowadays they are all done by machinery. In the intervening period the transportation of the coal through the horizontal tunnels was carried out by horses.

The main task for which ponies existed underground was known variously as putting, ganging or hauling. This, in simple terms, meant taking the empty tubs or small wagons from the main haulage system to the miners hewing at the coal-face, and bringing back the full ones to be taken by the main haulage to the shaft or pit bottom and thence to the surface. An uncomplicated and straightforward enough task, one would think, but a variety of factors made the job more or less difficult, awkward and dangerous.

Conditions at the coal-face and along the narrow passages or 'roads' leading to the face varied a good deal. The coal-hewers obtained their section of the face, called a 'stall' or 'heading' or 'stint' in a quarterly draw sometimes known as 'cavilling', and similarly the putters drew a 'flat' and two ponies, for the following three months. A 'flat' was the collecting place for the tubs from two or three stalls, and distances from stalls to flats varied considerably. Sometimes the distance for each journey could affect the putter's pay – he may, for instance, be given a basic wage per score of tubs at, say, 80 yards (the average journey for that pit), but be paid an increment as the distance increased to 100 and 120 yards or further. As the hewers would also be paid according to the number of tubs they filled, woe betide a putter who did not remove the full tubs and supply empty ones when required. Both hewer and putter placed a 'tally' on each tub so that their work could be accounted for.

For the putter each tally meant a series of manoeuvres carried out successfully. Here is a description of one journey at Marley Hill Colliery, as recounted by a miner who worked as a putter in the 1920s:

At the flat the pony's limbers were hooked onto the empty tub (sometimes two tubs, all depending on how the seam of coal ran, sometimes it was on the level, but sometimes it was a heavy pull out with full tubs). The pony would start off and when you came to the turn you had to go down, which the putter knew was near at hand, you would stop the pony, get past the tub, and pull the pony by the reins into the turning. The putter then had to guide the tub round the corner. When this was negotiated you went on a straight line again. When you arrived at the last turn before the coal-face, again you had to stop to get to the front to unhook the pony and send him on his way to the coal-face. While he was doing this you had to put the empty tub round the bend. You then went to the coal-face with the pony and hooked him onto a full tub, the front wheels being on the floor facing the coal-face, and two wheels on the plate, with the tub slightly on end. In this position the coal-hewers could fill the tub more easily. You then had to put your back to the tub – you bent your legs and grabbed the tub handles and lifted with your behind and arms, and this wasn't easy. Off you went, guiding the tub round the bend and stopping the pony. Then you pushed the empty tub to the face, doubled back to the tub and pony and held the tub with your hands on the handles to guide it round the corners. However, sometimes while the putter was taking the empty tub to the coal-face the pony would carry on and very often the putter would find the tub off the way and he would have to lift it back on. This was very heavy work, most of the lifting was done by behind and back, so when you had very little space between the top of the tub and the roof it made it very hard work getting the tub back onto the plates again.

Sometimes there was even less space at the face and 'siding over' had to be carried out:

When a pony drew its tubs into the stall end of the gate it was the practice for stallmen to push the carfles (car-fulls) back as near the coal-face as they could, for only at the face end of the gate was it wide enough to turn the empties over on their sides so that the full ones could pass and then there was less distance for the stallmen to shove the tubs into the coal-face gallery.

Some roadways were so narrow that the ponies themselves experienced difficulty turning round to face the other way, and a special technique emerged – here described by a Nottinghamshire miner: *'A pony would tuck his head between his front legs, turn slowly till his neck touched the sides, then bring his back legs in and spin like a top.'* Other ponies have *'virtually climbed up the side of a restricted roadway to turn round'.*

At least at the coal-face the boy putter might obtain brief assistance from the miners working there, but he and his pony had to face the conditions on the roadways alone. The roadways were simply tunnels equipped with rails, and their sole function was to allow the transport of the coal away from the face.

Roadway dimensions were never generous. If a pony and tub could scrape through without obvious injury, that would do. But roadways underground never remained the same. Convergence was a natural phenomenon, roadways got lower and narrower by the hour and invariably one would dint the floor or chip the roof, or both, to retain the original passage.

The narrowness was a constant hazard:

Tot was a very good worker, but he had a trick of stopping at a narrow place for five or ten minutes, and you could shout your head off but he wouldn't budge – you were stuck behind the tub and couldn't get at him!

Men known as 'wagonwaymen' or 'datallers' were employed to keep the roadways clear of fallen rock and wide and high enough for the tubs to pass through, but often the changing conditions were discovered the hard way by the putters, when a tub was derailed by loose rock on the rails, or, very frequently, when he found that his pony was scraping his collar and back on the roof. The situation was normally rectified by the wagonwayman 'dinting' or digging a hollow between the rails or even lowering the track, but several miners have spoken of their ponies taking their own precautions against suffering the pain of 'rooving' –

In all my career as a ganger I was never able to make an ostler believe that many animals, especially the old-stagers, were actually able to crouch whilst traversing low places, but it was true as day.

Another has commented on the low head-carriage of many pit ponies –

the reason for this became obvious after I became a pony driver, for the new entrants to the pit soon learned to keep their heads down after bumping their foreheads against the low roof bars in the workings.

A serious business, but one retired Midland miner remembered an old mining joke springing from it:

Then there was the ganger who complained of his

pony rooving and when the dataller began to take out some of the floor between the rails in that spot the lad said 'It's not there that he's catching, mester, it's on his back.'

Derailments were also caused when movement of the floor made the rails uneven, and frequent lifting of the tubs back onto the rails was a bane of the novice miner:

When I first began ganging on my own I recall suffering a lot from lifting sores at the bottom of my back. My mother used to vaseline them till such time as the skin grew tough as the palm of my hands.

A well-trained pony, though, could assist in the operation and ease the labour of the boy:

If the pony, told to 'Ease a bit', would lean into his collar, this was a great help – the easing forward of the pony, with the driver 'spragged' against the pull, made the lifting of the tubs much easier.

Another problem was the condition of the floor, which varied from dry stone and dust and coal-dust to the other extreme of water dripping from the roof and lying in the roadway.

And then the bloody water! Ponies wading through stinking sludge up to their bellies, falling into it, struggling frantically not to drown. Pony lads, myself included, kneeling in two feet of water, holding the pony's head up.

Other miners spoke of regularly working in six inches of water and the particular difficulties this caused, with ponies and boys unable to rely on a firm foothold. The gradients experienced, too, were a matter of major concern to the putters and of especial discomfort and danger to the ponies. In some collieries, such as Cannock Chase in the 1930s and Whitburn slightly earlier, the full tubs had to be pulled away from the face up inclines approaching 1 in 3, and two ponies in tandem had to be used. Less steep rises on the way to the flat would be overcome by a pony pulling and a boy pushing from behind. Before going up steep inclines the driver was required, at some collieries, to put a bar-hook on the back of the tub, to dig into the ground if the tub should run backwards and so prevent the pony being pulled backwards after it. The real danger, though, lay in the downhill slopes. Most workings enabled the ponies to pull empty tubs uphill so that the heavy full tubs were transported down the gradients. The ponies' job was to hold back the full tubs on the downward run by breeching or britching, whilst the putters helped in the operation by putting wooden 'lockers' through the rear wheels, preventing them from going round. This was done to lessen the chance of the heavy tubs overpowering the pony and pushing it forward too quickly. Sometimes, though, the lockers broke, or they were not put in properly, with the result that the pony was propelled forward out of control, likely to fall and unable to stop if it met an obstacle or a ventilation door.

Ventilation doors or 'air-doors' are part of the important system which regulates and controls the passage of fresh air round the mine. The air-doors open one way and the ponies are taught to open the doors by pushing in that direction as was discussed in Chapter III. When approaching from the other side the putter had to stop his pony and pull the doors open to allow them to pass through. A pony pushed by a runaway tub would not be able to stop and nasty accidents resulted.

On the subject of gradients a 19th century *Textbook of Coal-Mining* said: '*Not only is the useful affect reduced by adverse gradients, but the lives of the horses are considerably shortened; in a short space of time they become worthless, and the cost of upkeep is a serious matter.*'

When the full tub or tubs pulled by the putting pony arrived at a collecting point, there might already be a 'train' of full tubs assembled and the newly-arrived one had to be connected to it. The driver could either 'undog', or disconnect, his pony's limbers from the tub and then push the full tubs together, or he could wait until his pony was very close to the other tubs and then 'snatch off' the limbers from the tub and the pony would spin round, out of the way, allowing its tubs to run by him and onto the others.

22 Hot and humid conditions and hard work often meant that ponies were wet through with sweat. Marley Hill, 1971.

In some collieries conditions were very hot and humid. Miners worked nearly naked, wearing only shorts or pants – even cast-off french knickers have appeared below ground! – and the ponies, even though their manes and tails had been hogged, still suffered from the heat: '*The Kilburn seam was very hot, ponies and men sweated profusely and some of the ponies looked like skinned rabbits, so little hair did they grow.*' The sweating made the conditions even worse:

I sometimes still get a smell of sweating ponies in my nostrils. When we worked on inclines with full tubs that had to be spragged the pony-sweat smells were often nauseating. The smell of human sweat underground was often almost unbearable, but the pony sweat was sickening.

Rats, too, were occasionally a menace, existing in such numbers as to be disquieting to the ponies. In such pits the putters would wear bicycle-clips round their trousers, or use string, called 'Yorks', to ensure that the rats did not run up their trouser legs. When disturbed the rats would run along the rails in front of the pony and driver when, according to a Midland miner, *'gangers skimmed stones along the rail at rats they couldn't see, sometimes with considerable success'.*

A difficulty common to all mines was the fact of working in the dark. This is a darkness which, it must be remembered, is the pitch-black of the underground cave, quite different from the darkness experienced at night above ground. Underground, the darkness is complete and the eyes cannot make it seem less dark by becoming 'accustomed to it', as they can above ground. Miners recall days when their only light came from candles, fixed to the back of the tub by a 'sticking' of clay, and oil-lamps with reflectors brightened by metal-polish, and the arrival of the 'safety-lamp'. With all sources of light before the modern electric lamp a major problem underground was the relighting of a lamp which had been accidentally extinguished, for the means to relight it were very strictly controlled, and it is in this context that a particular mythology arose concerning the pit ponies. Many miners firmly believed that ponies could see in the pitch dark. Here are two of many illustrations of this belief:

So if your lamp should be put out you might have to wait for it to be lit again. There would be only one lighting station in the district and one man with a key to it. It meant you might have to go an hour or more without your lamp. You could not afford to wait, as you were on piece-work, so you just carried on in the dark. The pony would take you in and out. You had to find where your tokens were and the pony would take you to the empty tub in flat or siding, and on to the coal-face, where the men had their lamps.

You could let Rosie go four miles to the coal-face, by herself, along the travelling way where there was no danger from machinery. She would be there when you arrived, not a foot wrong in the dark. We could not go ten yards without a lamp.

This subject will be discussed further in Chapter VII, along with the so-called 'sixth-sense' of the ponies.

And in all these dark and difficult conditions, how much work was a pony expected to do? The actual weight of coal moved by a putting pony in a 7 or 8 hour shift obviously varied enormously according to the kind of mine, the geological conditions, the organisation of the work, the distance from face to flat, and so on. A Midland miner provided one set of figures: '*An average stall filled 6 tons apiece. 5 men at one stall equals 30 tons. 4 stalls per pony equals 120 tons.* $\frac{3}{4}$ *mile longest runs for tubstall ponies, 400 yards shortest.*'

Statistics employed by Engineers in the North of England quote much smaller figures, more like 27-30 tons per pony per day, with putting ponies only working over 180 yards distance.

If these figures are anything like accurate and average for their respective areas – and it must be remembered that Midland tubstall ponies were 14 h.h. animals and the Northern putting ponies quite likely to be 9 or 10 h.h. Shetlands – then it certainly sounds as if the ponies did a hard day's work, and probably a majority of collieries considered that enough was enough and the ponies would then be at rest for the remainder of the day. Sometimes, however, the work did not end after a shift. Ponies normally worked one shift on, one shift off, which usually meant 8 hours work a day, but it was by no means unknown for them to work more than this. At High Spen, for example, '*there were no substitutes, so if a pony was ill or injured, another pony would have to do his work for him in his "shift-off" time, so he would work three shifts in two days*'. The co-operative horses always suffered in such circumstances –

If a pony was a willing worker, and not bloody, it was taken out just about every shift. This wasn't supposed to happen, but it did, and was due to lack of supervision by horsekeepers and stablemen. As each shift started one very seldom saw a horsekeeper.

These are not isolated examples, for frequently the quarterly system, or cavilling, mentioned earlier, which was organised for the benefit of hewers and putters, required the ponies to do a double shift every other day:

The putter would draw a flat and two ponies. The ponies worked the three shifts. It meant that they had one 8 hour and one 16 hour shift, as the three putters shared the two ponies for the quarter.

There were five sets of brothers ganged on the district I was on, each set ganging the same stall and each working the same pony on days and nights. While we were on full time this meant that the pony was doing at least 11 shifts per week.

At least these ponies had the relative comfort and care of the stables at the end of their double shift. Not so at Clowne in the late 1920s:

Doctor and three or four more were kept down in the District from Monday morning till Saturday afternoon, and only saw the underground stables on Saturday afternoon and Sunday. Bags of corn were sent to feed them down the District. The reason for this was that the return airway wasn't big enough to let them travel to the stables and the main haulage was the only road they could travel. The Management would not or could not clear the tubs of coal off the haulage to let the horses have their deserved rest.

Besides putting, the other main occupation for ponies below ground was what was known as 'driving' in the North and 'stint' work or 'staging' elsewhere. This usually entailed taking the full tubs from the flat or pass-by where the putter had left them, to the point where they could be attached to the mechanical haulage which would pull them to the bottom of the shaft. In the early days of rope haulage the 'coffee-pot' engines were only capable of pulling the full tubs to the shaft and the empties and the haulage ropes had to be taken away from the engine by a pony which then followed the full ones back, and this job was also done by stint or driving ponies. When 'Main and Tail' haulage was introduced the empties were also taken in-bye, away from the shaft, mechanically.

Conditions in the main roadways were much better than those generally experienced by putting ponies and their drivers. The passageways were wider and higher, there were no roovings and few derailments, there were no steep gradients and conditions underfoot were usually good. Consequently more tubs could be pulled at one time and bigger animals could be used. Ponies up to 14 h.h. were common and in

23 A recent photograph showing a pit pony in full harness working in better conditions than those in illustration No. 22. Note the wider and higher road.

24 A controversial practice: a young boy 'rides the limmers' at Ashington Colliery in 1911. The dangers are evident from this photograph – one slip and the boy will be under the heels of the pony or the wheels of the tub.

the Midland collieries, before the Main and Tail systems were introduced, horses up to 16 h.h. were employed for main haulage work.

By the 1920s many collieries were stipulating that young boys, starting work underground, could only work as drivers at first, and it was commonly recognised that putting was one of the hardest (some miners said *the* hardest) and most unpleasant jobs in the pit. At the age of 18 boys were given the chance of putting if there were vacancies. It is worth noting that at Kilburn Pit in the 1930s full-grown men were employed on ganging:

When I got to Kilburn – the only pit on full time, the ponies were making 12 and 13 shifts a week. By the weekend I was having to shove my pony back to the stable, and quite a lot of the men were. Although pony work till then had always been considered a boys' job they found with the conditions there it took a man to do it, there was that much lifting and that much dirt to shift because of the bad strata, and it was the Kilburn Seam that got the nick-name 'Kill'em' because there was a pony killed there about every week and quite a few men in a year.

At Cresswell Colliery in the 1920s ponies taking out empty tubs at the beginning of the shift were also required to provide transport for the hewers on their way to work:

Each pony would take a tub with four or five miners to the coal-face. The drivers would hitch onto a wooden tub, hang a light onto the front of it, and sit on the steel limmers. Four men sat on the floor of the tub and sometimes a fifth squeezed in. How those ponies used to trot and gallop between the sleepers was uncanny – very rarely did one stumble – for our lights hung on the sides of the tub and swung all the way and there were no other lights.

Supplies and gear for repair and salvage work were also transported by ponies and, as seen in Chapter II, it is for these kinds of jobs that the last few ponies working underground in the 1980s, are kept. In the days of putting and driving ponies one or two older animals might be kept on for these lighter jobs or, as repair work was often done at weekends out of shift hours, a regular working pony would be required to do overtime. Although these jobs did not normally entail the pulling of heavy wagons the work was usually awkward and inconvenient. Repair journeys were made along the 'travelling roads', which were usually old ex-haulage roads now only used to enable workers to travel to the face, for the main haulage roads were never used for anything but coal haulage, except in emergencies. The travelling roads were always in need of attention and were often closing up and becoming low and difficult to move along. (One miner pointed out how '*at the outbreak of war every experienced man was moved to the coal-face and within a couple of years some of these travelling roads were little more than 3 feet high and the men were having to crawl long distances*'.)

Most of the supplies, repairs and salvage jobs were done by ponies wearing 'tracing' or 'slung' gear instead of limbers. This meant that they pulled a steel chain or leather straps with a hook on the end, which could be hooked onto, or fastened round, any shape of object – rocks, girders, props, anything large could be pulled in traces, whereas limbers were only of use in hauling wagons. In sling gear, too, it was possible to use two ponies in tandem, one behind the other, to haul larger loads, but in practice this was very seldom done, and a reason is offered in the following account:

With narrow gates, and on a steep incline one pony couldn't pull the cutting machine, so we fetched the other pony, in sling gears, and hung it on the front, but we couldn't get the ponies to pull together, as the men had to be right behind, or right in front. On the surface, with a hay-wain, the drivers could lead both horses from the side, but in a narrow gate there wasn't room.

The best position for a driver to enable him to control a pony pulling a tub or train through roadways with restricted width and height was always a thorny problem. Frequently there was not room to lead from the accepted place at the side of the pony's head, and '*to lead from in front of the animal was asking to get your heels trodden on*'.

It was common practice, when there was headroom and when the tubs were empty, for the driver to climb into the front tub and direct operations from there. If the tubs were full the driver had the alternatives of steering from behind – some tubs had handles to help the putters to steer them round the corners and lift them after derailments or siding over operations – or 'riding the limbers'. This meant that the putter sat on the 'iron' where the shafts converged, and rode precariously perched between the pony's tail and the front of the tub. Many miners have said that there was really no alternative to riding the limbers in the conditions under which they worked, and that this was always done, despite the obvious discomfort and danger, particularly where the circumstances allowed the pony to move quickly, as they certainly did at times. A Midland miner explained a secondary reason for the practice: '*The turns were so sharp off the crossgates into the stallgates that if the ganger did not ride the iron, and lean outwards like a dinghy sailor, the first tub always jumped the rails.*'

The strange fact that emerges, though, is that in many pits 'riding the limbers' was expressly forbidden by the colliery management, and miners could be penalised if they were caught doing it, even if some officials apparently turned a blind eye: '*It was against the pit rules, but only the manager ever enforced it – penalty 2s. 6d to the local hospital.*'

It is obvious from this consideration of the work done by the pit ponies and the conditions in which they did it that a well-trained, willing and knowledgeable pony could be a great help to his driver, whilst an awkward or badly trained animal could be a worrying handicap. Different animals had different strengths and weaknesses: '*I had a district. I was in charge of 8 horses and drivers – you'd have perhaps 2 breeching horses, 2 pullers, 2 idle sods ...*' and they would be employed where their strengths could be capitalised on and their weaknesses hidden. The knowledgeable ponies might well contribute more than might reasonably be expected of them and many miners have recalled individual ponies with particular skills. A few examples are quoted here in the hope that they will emphasise the often overlooked individuality of pit ponies at work.

Punch made my work so easy; he knew where to stop without my speaking. I would jump off the shaft-iron and turn the point, then go and get back on the shaft-iron again. He would go forward and open the two doors with his head, going into the stall, but coming out again he would stop, because he knew it was the other way round.

Now when we came out with the second and subsequent tubs, Taffy would go as far as he could with this tub and stop with his chest touching the tub in front of him. I would take the limbers off and without a word from me Taffy would go round to the back of the tub and give it a push with his chest until it bumped into the other one, and I coupled them together. This system was carried on all the shift, and without Taffy I would have had to push all those tubs myself – and remember there was a ton of stone in each.

When you took his limmer hook off the full tubs, instead of crossing to the empty tubs he would stand still till I moved, then he would follow me across like a dog at heel, then back up until his limmers touched the tub.

I used to take six tubs from No. 1 to No. 2; it was up a hill and I had to take the chains off the tubs before they ran down an incline. Never once did I over-run, because Daisy my pony knew just where to step into the side for me to take the chains off, and then he would go back on his own through three sets of ventilation doors, pushing the doors open with his nose, back into the pit bottom for another run.

Bumble could tell the difference between a set of tubs running under control or running free. He worked at the bottom of an incline, and if they broke loose he would chase his driver out of the flat. The only trouble was that he would carry on to the stables and that was his lot for the shift.

Many ponies learned where to stop for lockers to be put into the wheels, or learned not to pull over open switches or incorrect points on the rails – even in the dark of dim lamplight. Some learned their limitations and found ways of ensuring that they were not exceeded; the description of Bumble who '*could even count the number of tubs he had to pull as they were hooked together by steel couplings; a certain number, and no more*' and Mick, whose job '*was to trace tubs up to make a set. He would pull only one tub at a time, and even if I tried to keep the couplings tight in adding a second – even an empty timber tub – he wouldn't pull until one was taken off*' are two of dozens of examples of horses who had '*the ability to judge to a fine point just how much work they will do before they say 'enough' – and ask them to pull one ounce extra and all four feet become anchored to the ground and dynamite wouldn't move them*'.

Perhaps on occasion this individuality was taken too far, as with Sam, who '*worked best if his driver played a mouth-organ which he kept strung round his neck. One day he forgot it, and there was no progress from Sam until a comb and paper was substituted*' or the pony at Bowburn – '*The overman in one shift always took that pony an apple, and that pony used to walk into that office and wouldn't go out until he got his apple.*'

Playing the mouth-organ and providing titbits suggest a good relationship between ponies and men. This was not always the case, and tales of cruelty abound. Whilst it is necessary to illustrate the facts of the cruel behaviour, in order to give an all-round picture, it is also important to be aware of the kind of chain of events that might lead to it. A miner who worked in Hartley pit in the early 1900s explained the situation very well, and is worth quoting at length:

I always felt sorry for the pit ponies that were ill-treated, but to me the system was to blame. The majority of cases brought to court were about putting ponies. The putter was paid so much per tub depending on the distance from the flat or landing to the coal-face. When taking the empty tub in, it had to be put in a siding, while we went in to get the full tub. A good pony would stay put just past the siding, to let you take the empty tub into the face. But another pony would walk away to a place where the putter could neither get past the side nor over the top of the tub, so after throwing stones or coal at him to get him to move, the putter eventually had to go to the face and down the next roadway to get round to the pony. As this took a lot of time and his wage depended on the number of tubs, he would lose his temper and ill-treat the pony.

The frustration is understandable, and there is no doubt that there were awkward and difficult ponies like this, though they were, by all accounts, only a very small minority, as were, no doubt, the miners who ill-treated them. Some handlers were very cruel –

I have seen coal putters lose their tempers if things were not going right for them. Often I have seen them pick up a wooden 'dreg' and smash into the pony's ribs and hit it across the head. The pony would throw its head up to avoid further punishment, only to bang its head on the roof.

I'll never forget that first day. After I got the pony yoked up he was kicking and shivering and he would not pull, and then he just flopped onto the bottom. Two old night-shift stone-men came onto the scene – 'Don't worry, son, we'll get him to pull for you'. They just picked up their shovels and brayed it till it got up. All the time I've worked with ponies I've seen them badly used.

Beating the ponies to get them to work was the commonest ill-treatment, and in some collieries the drivers were issued with a short whip, '*about six inches of hickory shaft and a plaited leather thong of about eight inches*'. At times these were over-employed, and some miners found them of little use for the job for which they were intended, although they did, strangely, become 'a sort of status symbol'. The whips did serve other purposes: '*You could insert the shaft into the aperture 'fore the limbers rod at rear or in front, so that it became a hand-lever for lifting the tub onto the way.*' Until forbidden by the NCB twitches hung in many stables for use with difficult horses. A twitch is a leather thong in the shape of a loop which is twisted round the horse's upper lip – an age-old method of controlling difficult or dangerous animals for shoeing, medical treatment and so on, but is none the less painful for that.

Some sadistic drivers found more insidious ways of 'encouraging' stubborn animals. At a landing the electric bell wires could be used to give a pony a shock, and the cruel practice of pushing a piece of coal into a horse's anus has been mentioned many times – this latter action being based upon the theory that a pony, feeling the pain and discomfort at its rear end would move forward to try and get away from it.

Deliberate ill-treatment of animals is, of course, against the law of the land and is a criminal offence whether committed above or below ground. If a case of a driver behaving cruelly to a pit pony was brought to the notice of the management, either by another miner reporting the driver, or by the horsekeeper finding evidence of the ill-treatment on the pony, a court case could result. A Welsh miner recalled such an occurence:

A driver in a temper put his hand into a pony's mouth and twisted his tongue, injuring the animal quite badly and it had to go for treatment to the surface for roughly three weeks. The driver went to court and was sentenced to six months in prison for cruelty, and when he came out no colliery would employ him.

Newspaper reports from the 1890s preserved at Clifton Colliery show that in those days and in that pit cruelty was the rule rather than the exception, and the court was the means the management used to provide a deterrent, though not, it would seem, very successfully. At the Summons Court reported on 17 March, 1897 the

RSPCA Inspector, who brought the prosecution on behalf of the colliery, said that '*the management wished the Bench to make an example of these lads. The ponies in the pit were very ill-treated and they had difficulty getting at the culprits.*'

The three boys brought before the court charged with cruelty had all been seen beating ponies, and were each fined 20 shillings, a very considerable sum in those days. A year later the colliery officials again prosecuted through the RSPCA Inspector and 'pressed for a severe penalty' on a charge of extreme cruelty. The 17-year-old youth was found guilty and sent to prison for 21 days for beating a pony until it fell down. The *Daily Guardian* report on the case is most revealing concerning the general conditions at the colliery. The would-be deterrent of the previous year's fines had been unsuccessful:

as those examples seemed to have had little effect in stopping the cruelty. It was difficult to detect lads in the act, as they were not always under observation and they presumed upon it. Almost daily, ponies were brought back to the stables injured and bearing other evidence of being unmercifully used.

At least by the 1920s the situation throughout the industry would seem to have improved upon the Clifton example, and the cases of cruelty that did arise seem to have been dealt with below ground rather than in the courts. A considerable number of miners have said that the welfare of the ponies was protected by the other drivers:

Bully-boys ill-treating the ponies or taking it out on them were dealt rough justice by the other driver-lads, who would not snitch to the horsekeepers or deputies – which would only lose the bully his job – but thump or wet or rub the culprit with manure etc.

I have seen fists flying when young drivers have seen someone ill-treating a pony.

Now and again some bad-tempered putter would do something, but woe betide him if the decent blokes saw him.

It would seem general practice that the average workman would interfere if he saw ill-treatment of the ponies, and the amount of cruelty seems to have diminished over the years, possibly as conditions improved. Certainly by the 1930s and 1940s some miners were able to say

Occasionally a pony was beaten, but mostly they were shown kindness, and I have seen young lads pulling their guts out to assist the ponies.

They were worked hard, but they weren't hammered into the ground, and they weren't badly treated.

or even

I can honestly say that during my lifetime in the pits I never saw any driver deliberately ill-treating his pony.

The opposite extreme from the cruelty might be seen in a comment from a miner who worked at South Garesfield Colliery in the 1930s: '*Treatment of ponies at this colliery while I was there couldn't possibly have been better; they were pets, pure and simple.*' Memory plays tricks, and distance in time can lend enchantment to the view, but the overall picture that emerges from the evidence is of enormous variation in the treatment of the ponies by their handlers, according to such factors as management attitudes, officials' efficiency, conditions of work, pressures of employment and the simple fact that all horses are different and all men are different.

It is worth noting, in passing, that the 'ill-treatment' was not all one way – '*Some of the ponies would take advantage of the nervous young lads, and when they were unhooked from a set of tubs they would chase them down the road!*' Less amusing is the story of Press, a stallion which worked at Whitburn Colliery:

Because of the need to keep up to the average number of tubs – 18 – when on piecework I've not let him stop for water during my shift. He had a habit of kicking when free of his tubs, and he got his revenge one day when, as I turned him from a full tub to an empty one I was a second too slow and he caught me a glancing kick in the face which needed nine stitches.

At the end of a shift, ponies and handlers left the working districts to return to the stables. At many collieries this was in the nature of a stampede. A Midland miner describes the scene at his pit:

The workmen, ponies and drivers were allowed out of the workings to a meeting place on the main road, about ¾ mile from the stables. No-one was allowed past this point till 2.30p.m. or when two 8s was rung on the haulage bell. The drivers would bring their ponies to this point, lift the harness off the pony's back and put it over its head onto its neck. Then the drivers would get behind the ponies and wait for the bell to ring. There would be as many as 20 or 30 ponies waiting. Nobody moved and the ponies stood patiently waiting. Suddenly the bell would start ringing and every pony would set off at a gallop for the stables. 30 ponies going at a gallop in the roadway 9 feet wide and 5 feet high – you can understand why the drivers didn't get in front. It was like the charge of the Light Brigade in pitch darkness. The drivers had put the harness round the ponies' necks to prevent it slipping and tripping the pony up in the charge.

With the journey back to the stables often a distance of two miles or more it is not surprising that, when the roof height allowed it, the drivers were tempted to ride the ponies back to the stables. This was strictly against all colliery rules, but very frequently the risk of being caught was taken and the lads did ride – particularly when the pony was likely to go off like a rocket back to the stables, leaving his driver behind and in line for more trouble from the horsekeeper for not taking proper care of the pony. Deputies and horsekeepers tried to catch culprits riding the ponies, but identification was usually a problem in the dark roadways and ingenious methods were thought up. Miners from several coalfields told versions of the following incident:

One day four drivers who'd been riding and thought they'd got away with it were sent to the office to see the manager. Upon interrogation they admitted it and were fined and threatened with the sack. They came out saying that somebody had 'shopped' them, but no workman worth his salt ever would. It was the horsekeeper. He had taken a can of whitewash into a manhole at the side of the roadway, turned off his light, and when a ridden pony had gone by he had sprayed whitewash onto the pony's backside, unknown to the rider. When all the ponies were back in the stable the ostler looked to see which ponies had whitewash on them and he knew which drivers had been riding.

In their anxiety to be back at the stables quickly drivers were prepared to take all sorts of risks, but possibly the most foolhardy is contained in this description from Brancepeth Colliery:

One particular seam, all the men used to come out on the 'run', then the driver lads had to bring the ponies out, they weren't allowed in front of the run, so the lads used to stand on the ropes and have the ponies stretched out alongside the ropes. It was illegal and dangerous – they used to bump over the rollers, they could have had a leg taken off. They stood on the ropes and held onto the pony to keep balance.

It is a relief to contrast this with the more reasonable scene drawn from Cannock Chase in the 1930s: '*If the handler stayed over to repair rails at the end of the shift he would untackle the pony and it would walk out with the faceworkers till it reached the stables about two miles away.*' There is something very comradely and appropriate in the picture of pony and miners walking away from work together – taken a stage further in this amusing example of end-of-shift behaviour from Derbyshire:

When I first started at Top Hard all that we used to have for transport at the end of the shift was about 40 flat-bottomed trams. You used to sit back-to-back, four men. It only went at about 4 miles per hour, and I've seen some of the horses stand or sit on some of these trams, coming back from the district. Some would sit, just like one of those circus ponies, and some would just stand.

5 Life Underground - Stabling and Harness

Stabling

In 1936 I went down the mine at Seghill with my husband and a Swiss friend. My most vivid memory of this is the well-lit, spotless conditions of the stalls and the ponies so well cared for and contented. Their names were painted above the stalls and the animals were untethered. The horsekeeper gave me some sugarlumps and told me to call any names I liked to choose. As I did those ponies trotted over to me for sugar. A pat on the neck and a gentle order to go back to their stalls resulted in each pony returning to its proper place. Our Swiss friend commented 'Now I see how you English love animals.'

The stable was a long, unlit gallery, 50 or 60 yards long, 10 feet wide and 8 feet high. Each horse had a stall with a wooden box on the wall for a manger. The stalls were divided by wooden partitions. The whole place stank to high heaven of droppings and urine. The urine ran into a gutter behind the horses and was just left to soak into the floor. The horses, tired out after working just lay down in their own filth.

Resting conditions, like working conditions, differed enormously from colliery to colliery, though there seems to have been a good majority of well-kept stables, clean, spacious and comfortable. The stables seem all to have been laid out in very similar fashion with the stalls down one side of a wide corridor, much the same as stables above ground. Sometimes the walls and roof would be bare rock, or even coal, but often – particularly in the larger stables for up to a couple of hundred horses – the walls would be bricked out. Dividing partitions were usually wooden but again, in some of the bigger stables, they would be of brick, whilst at Hordern Colliery, for example, the stalls were separated by swinging wooden arms on a chain support. Each stall would have a manger or box for food, and sometimes a water container (the alternative was a common trough or barrel to which the ponies were taken to drink). The roadway behind the stalls may be fitted with rails to allow a small wagon to be used for distribution of food or to carry away soiled bedding. Just occasionally, at the smaller collieries, the ponies had the luxury of loose-boxes which gave them added freedom and the opportunity to roll.

Most of the stables were kept very clean, either because the horsekeepers themselves took pride in the care of their animals, or because the management insisted that they did so:

The under-manager in those days was very strict; he thought more about the ponies than the men. In fact every morning he would inspect the stables but I can quite honestly say I have never seen any stable look as clean. You could have eaten off the floor, as they say.

Many miners compared conditions in the pit stables very favourably with riding stables and similar establishments above ground, and if the fact that the pit ponies were kept in stalls all the time they were not working seems limiting, it is worth bearing in mind that in the days when horses did all the transporting and pulling in the city and country, the vast majority were confined to stalls in their resting period. Loose-boxes and freedom in fields for horses has only become the norm since horses became luxury and leisure accessories; working animals didn't live like that. The cleanliness of underground stables is

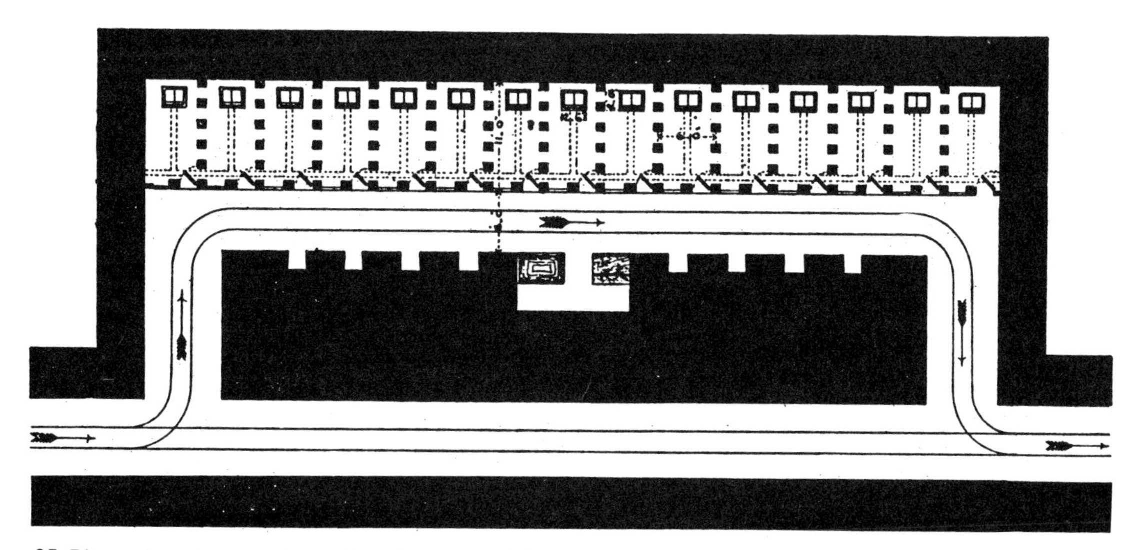

25 Plan of underground stables, from a mining textbook of 1898.

Although both plans are of stalls the 1935 plan has a number of improvements; the rails are at both ends of a stall, for both cleaning and feeding; there are extra water-troughs, electric lights and rooms for harness storage and repair, and for the storage of feed or 'choppy'.

26 Plan of underground stables, from a haulage manual of 1935.

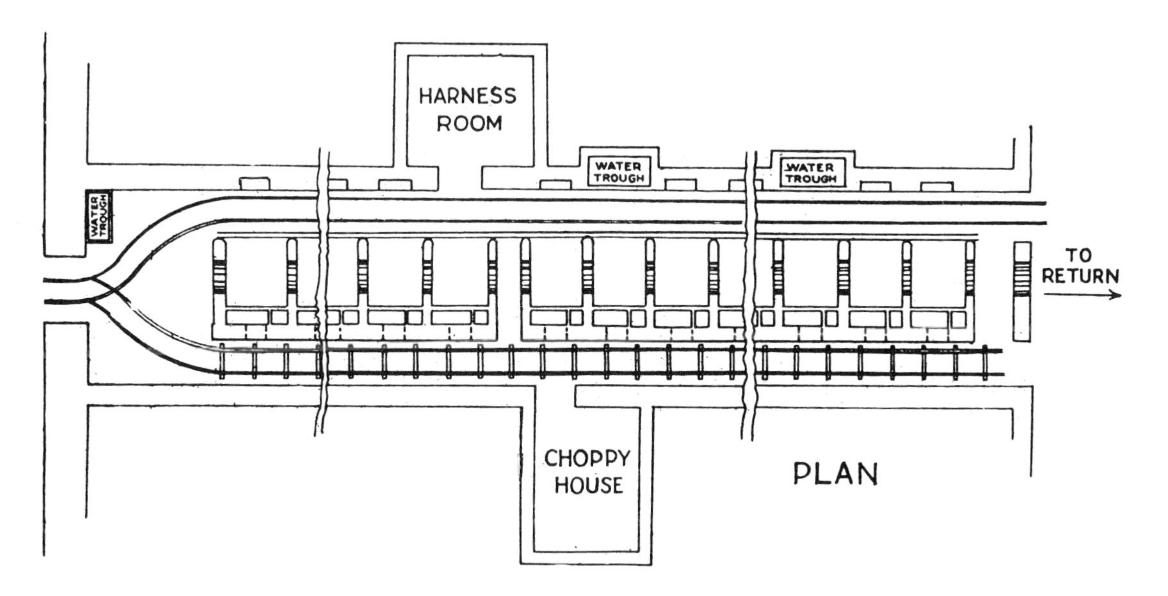

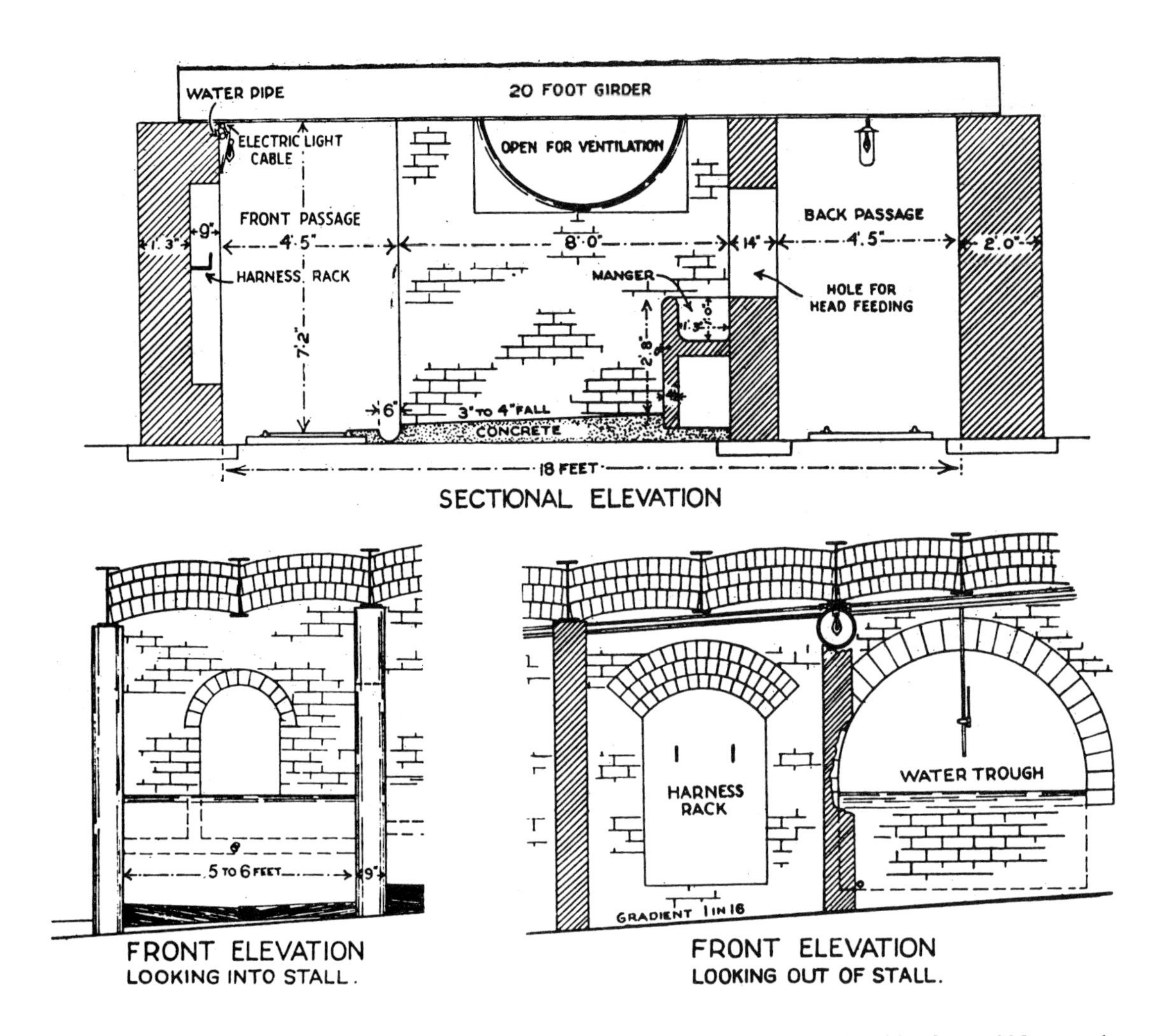

27 Detail of underground stables from 1935 manual.

underlined by the common practice of white-washing walls and roof, as often as six times a year. An interesting variation on this, carried out at Langwith Colliery, was to paint the stables green – '*It looked good, it did. A bit like grass, you see.*'

The aim in the stables was obviously to try to create conditions in which the ponies would remain healthy and would be able to rest. The provision of suitable flooring and bedding therefore was an important factor and exercised the minds of many officials. A Mr Blackett, for example, wrote in 1902:

Mr Charles Hunting, in his paper on the feeding of underground horses, is responsible for the statement that only 1 in 10 lie down on brick, 2 in 10 on cement with sawdust and 7 in 10 on wood. This, the writer thinks, can only refer to very large horses, as he is not aware of a single case in the collieries under his charge, of an animal which does not regularly lie down.

Another engineer wrote that straw should not be used because of the fire-risk and that peat and sawdust were best, except that moss-litter should be used '*to prevent injury in violent colic or where mine-drainage is poor*'. In fact sawdust seems to have been most commonly used for bedding, on a concrete floor. This was comfortable for the pony, convenient for the horsekeepers and cheap for the management.

28 Lambton D Pit.

Ventilation was also important. A good supply of fresh air was needed; at the same time the stables needed keeping warm but not so oppressive that the animals could not sleep. A balance was not always achieved: *'The ventilation was diabolical, it was hot as hell'* but in many places the effort to do so was considerable. A separate ventilation system, between the intake and the return, was usually the solution, with a means of regulation as an added sophistication:

If I thought it was getting a bit too warm I used to ease the hole at the top of the stable, where the air went out. When we had a new pony come down the pit you had to put him at the top end, 'cos if he has any kind of disease, an infectious disease, like strangles, it'd go away from the other ponies. Keep him there till you're sure he was alright.

Lighting used to be by hurricane lamps, sometimes hung from a wire that ran the length of the stable. There they gave a general light and could be detached by a horsekeeper and used for closer inspection when needed. The horsekeeper would put the lamps out as he left, so that the ponies had a period of darkness to sleep in. With the onset of electric lights it became more usual to leave the lamps on all the time, particularly if it was felt that the lights gave a necessary boost to the warmth of the stable. *'Our ponies don't know night from day as they are never in the dark, but they do know their shifts and like any other horses they know their feed times.'*

Whatever effect the nationalisation of the coal mines had on other aspects of the coal industry there can be little doubt that as far as the pit ponies were concerned the change was for the better. *'The change that struck me most'*, said one Derbyshire miner, *'was the stables down the pit – a different atmosphere seemed to exist.'*

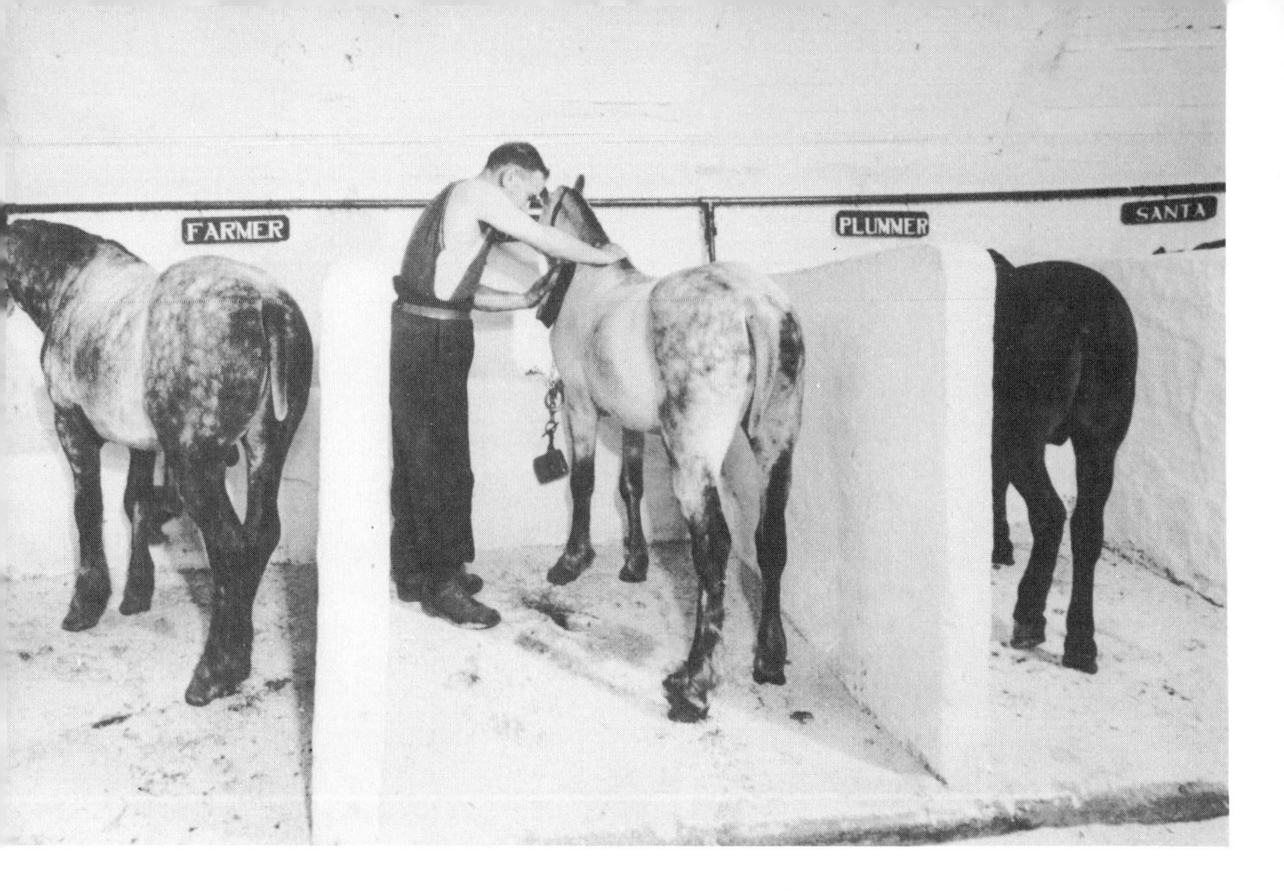

29 Hordern Colliery.

28, 29 Two different pre-war underground stables (illustration No. 39 shows a third) all showing the same basic characteristics contained in the 1898 plan: stall accomodation, with mangers (and water laid on in Nos. 28, 39); drainage channels, rails for cleaning and feeding. Note also the name-plates, and the harness-racks at the back of each standing.

Disinfectant foot-baths for the ponies, regular white-washing of the walls and general tightening up of regulations replaced *'filth, dank air and stench'* in another Midland mine. Another feature of the change-over was a war on vermin in the stables.

Warmth, darkness and the presence of food meant that once vermin got into the stables they multiplied rapidly and tales of plagues of rats, cockroaches (or 'blackclocks'), mice and flies abound. Most stables kept a few cats in an attempt to keep the rat population down and sometimes they were successful in clearing the stables and improving the ponies' rest – but at the cost of inconvenience to men and animals down in the districts, where the rats went to escape the cats! Sometimes, though, the rats were victorious; a number of miners spoke of cats killed by rats in the stables. So bad did the situation become at times that horsekeepers were given a price per tail (a shilling for 8, in Wales in the 1920s) by the company, to encourage the trapping of rats. The following anecdote describes the situation graphically: a miner sometimes worked as 'escort' to the deputy making the Sunday evening inspection of the stables, at the entrance to which was an almost empty feed tub awaiting transport to the surface:

This is where I came in, with my brick. We would stop and listen. In the silence and blackness we could hear rustling and squeaking coming from the tub, and I would throw my brick into it. All hell was let loose. Out of that tub, screaming – yes, screaming – came the rats; there must have been 50 or more in that tub-bottom, eating the left-overs ... As we entered the stables the rats ran before us in droves, up the walls, over the standings, through the mangers and over the horses, most of which were lying down. The horses never flinched, they were used to the rats. I was 14 and it frightened me to death.

Cockroaches, a large version of which were called 'blackclocks' by the miners, also existed in tens of thousands in some colliery stables. Ostlers at Welbeck were issued with flails – pieces of leather 12 inches long and 9 inches wide attached to a wooden handle – in an attempt to control the numbers. '*Every time you walked into a stable, especially them up the district, you could hear the blackclocks clatter.*' They usually just had to be endured, but occasionally they were exterminated. In one pit an invasion of rats destroyed all the cockroaches! In another the cockroaches died of starvation during the 1926 strike, when the ponies were all taken above ground for 26 weeks and so no food was taken into the stables – '*then we shovelled them up in millions.*' A successful method utilised in some North-Eastern collieries was a steam-pipe with a narrow jet which would kill the cockroaches and had the advantage of being able to get into the narrow crannies where the insects lived.

Normally other insects were not a problem. Flies, a major nuisance to horses above ground, did not usually trouble pit ponies, but there were exceptions even to this, as the following intriguing tale explains:

One summer the stables were plagued with millions of flies, and all the hostlers were kept busy for weeks with little rubber bats, swatting them. What could be done to shift them? One Sunday morning the manager had all the 140 ponies taken up the roads, then had men open all the ventilation doors between down and upcast shafts. It worked! Those on the pit top saw a huge buzzing black cloud that almost obliterated the upcast headstocks before being wafted up into the blue!

Stalls usually had a place for the pony's name to be placed. This would often be only a piece of wood smooth enough for the horsekeeper to write the name in chalk, but painted name-plates were not unknown. Horses often occupied the same stall for many years – outstaying several generations of putters – and some permanence for the name-plate was not a bad thing. The naming of the horses in the first place makes an interesting study. Sometimes it was a case of a new pony simply taking over a stall and adopting the name already painted over it. Often the pony was given a name from the current affairs of the time – one miner recalls the older ponies in his pit bearing names from the Boer War – Botha, Kruger, Baden, etc. – whilst the manager's interests are revealed in horses named Jardine and Larwood in the year of the Bodyline controversy! The name could be used to help with the records of the stable, as in the collieries where batches of incoming horses were all given names beginning with the same letter of the alphabet, and the next batch would get the next letter, and so on, so that the names indicated the age of the pony and how long it had been at the pit. This is a system commonly used in dairy herds and might well have been copied from farming.

The officials may have chosen names according to some system, but, like the stud-book names of pedigree animals, the pit ponies' 'official' names were in some collieries seldom used: '*The manager said he thought that ponies answered better to a two syllabled name, little realising, I suppose, that very few ponies ever got called by their "given" name.*' Or, as another miner put it –

Every horse had his stable name on his standing. That was his proper name, that he was written down as. But then he had a working name – the first lad to take him out, perhaps he fancied a certain name, so he called him that, and they passed it on. I expect it was the same at all pits, they'd have stable and district names.

Stables had to be built fairly early in the development of a mine, and so were usually near the shaft. As the workings spread further and further so the journey for men and ponies from the shaft to the coal-face increased accordingly, until the ponies could be spending an inordinately large proportion of each shift actually

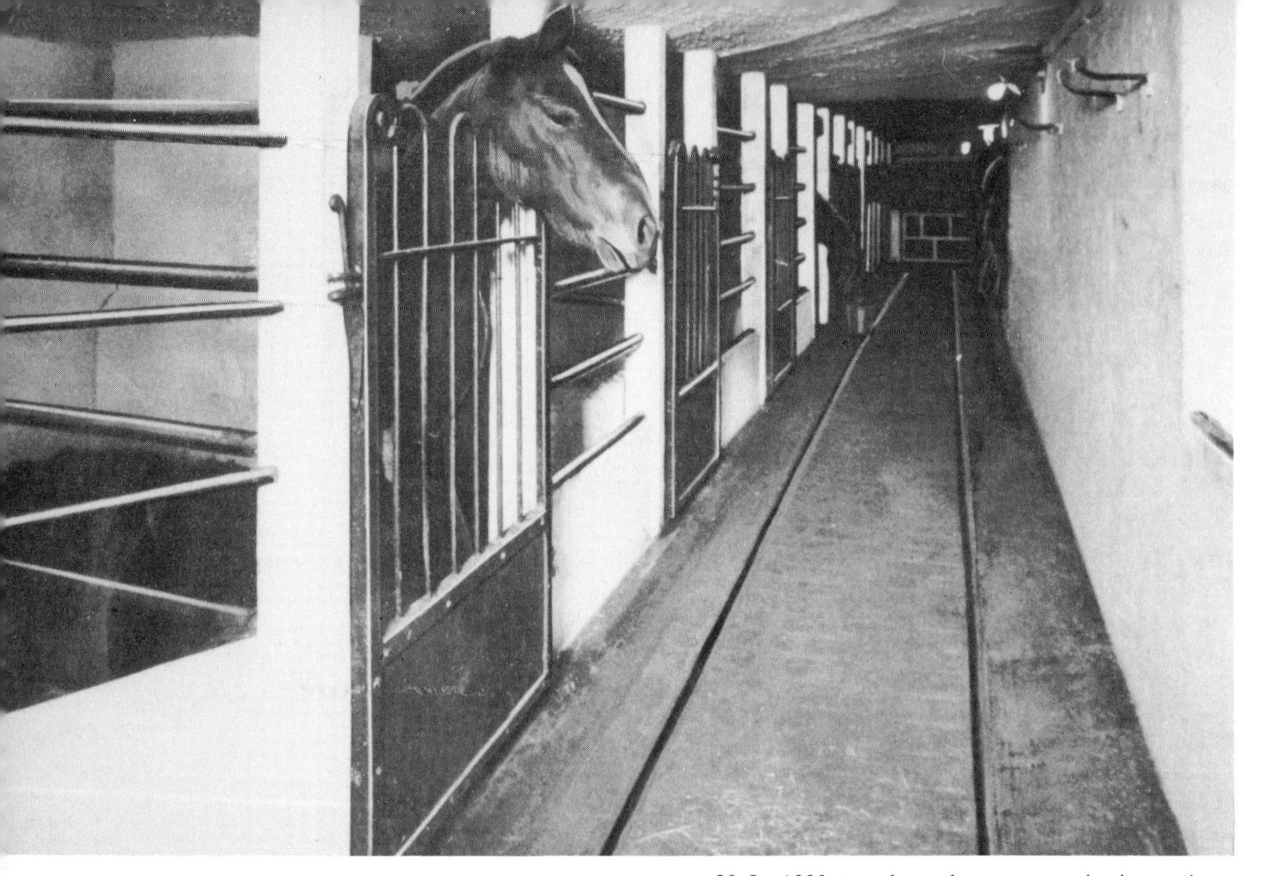

30 In 1933 new loose boxes, necessitating a 'large reconstruction scheme', were provided at Bomarsand Colliery by the Bedlington Coal Company. The work was said to have been 'praised by Her Majesty's Inspector of Pit Horses'. These railed boxes certainly look very smart, and gave the ponies more freedom of movement, but would undoubtedly have made the work of the horsekeepers more arduous.

walking to and from their place of work. Secondary stables were therefore built 'inbye', near the working districts, to cut down the travelling time. Ellington Colliery is a good example of this. The magnificently built stables at the pit bottom housed 150 ponies in the days of pony-putting, but the working faces moved some 3½ miles from the main shaft, and stables for 50 ponies were made in the early 1970s to accomodate the ponies still employed at the pit for supply and salvage work.

As the phasing out of the ponies got underway and collieries retained only a handful of ponies it became more convenient and economic to house the survivors at the pithead and to transport them down and up the shaft each day with their drivers. Some collieries have always stabled their horses above ground – nearly all drift mines (mines entered by a horizontal tunnel into a hillside, without a shaft) did so, and the stables sometimes formed an integral part of the pit-village attached to the mine: '*The stables were at the end of the street. Boys mucked out at nights and weekends, a bit like a riding school. The feeding was good, and the ponies got tit-bits extra.*'

Harness

On the wall at the back of each pony's stall there were usually pegs or hooks on which to hang the pony's harness. Most of the leather gear worn by pit ponies was the same as, or similar to, that worn by draught horses above ground, as can be seen in the illustration on p.36. An obvious difference is the head-gear worn by pit ponies. Above ground the head harness consisted of bridle and blinkers, which were used to prevent the animal being distracted or frightened by things happening to the side of it. Underground this was not so important, there being fewer

31 Two ponies wearing only 'skull-caps', which were not permitted after 1911, as they afforded no eye protection.

distractions, but what did matter was that the top of the head and the eyes should be protected if and when the pony banged against obstructions in the walls and roof of the roadways. The design of these eyeshields and 'bonnets' varied considerably, as can be seen from the illustrations. Most were made of thick leather but there is evidence of steel bars being incorporated both in the bonnet and as a grille to protect the eyes. In the 1930s there were a number of experiments exploring the possibility of the ponies carrying their own headlights instead of having to rely upon the illumination provided by the driver's lamp, which was usually well behind the pony. Some experiments had had to wait until battery-powered lamps were available, but even then they were not successful. The lamp was attached to a slit in the bonnet and later, when this was found not to be acceptable, lamps were tried attached to the collar, but this idea, too, was

32 Pony and driver in 1926. Note the extended form of the 'skull-cap', giving more protection to the forehead and the eyes.

abandoned, despite the interest of several parties. The *Colliery Guardian* in 1931 wrote that '*An experiment is being conducted at Sharleton West Colliery, with headlamps for horses, and at least two other firms are seriously considering the matter.*' By the mid 1930s the experiments seem to have come to an end. A miner who had been involved in the trials said:

The lamps we tried were fitted to the bottom of the collar and were regarded as a great gimmick, but to ponies who had worked in semi-darkness for years they proved a liability. The flashing light threw shadows which made the pony unsure of himself, and, as the ponies frequently 'breasted' the tubs with the bottom of the collar, the lamp got in the way. It either got smashed or had to be removed each time the manoeuvre was repeated. After a trial period the lamps were removed and the idea abandoned.

Another variation from normal harness was the use of a rein on one side only, or no rein at all and the possible absence of a bit. At one Derbyshire mine a bit was only used on new ponies 'that couldn't be trusted'; the rest had the bit put behind the lower jaw out of the way. A further oddity was a leather 'backskin' to keep the ponies dry in mines which had 'top water' roadways where water dripped from the roof.

The harnessing of ponies was sometimes done by the horsekeepers and sometimes by the drivers. It was of great importance to the horse's welfare that the harnessing was done correctly, for ill-adjusted harness could quickly result in sores under collars and chafing-straps. The major drawbacks were harness that was not in good condition or didn't fit properly, and boys who did not know how the job should be done. '*It was most essential that collars, breeching straps and pulling chains were evenly balanced. If not the pony would pull more on one side than the other, thus creating a very sore shoulder.*' The tack took a lot of punishment in the conditions of work underground and was frequently broken. Damaged harness had to be reported to the Deputy or to the horsekeeper, who was then responsible for getting it repaired. In some pits the horsekeeper himself did saddlery repairs, but it was more normal for the work to be sent out to a local saddler or for the company, if big enough, to employ its own. The letter reproduced on p.63 indicates the importance of the amount of saddlery purchases and repairs both to the collieries and the tradesmen concerned. The change from using 'outside firms' to creating their own saddlery repair shop must have been exercising the minds of cost-conscious managers round the country at the time of those letters, the 1920s, as there is further evidence from a Midland Colliery:

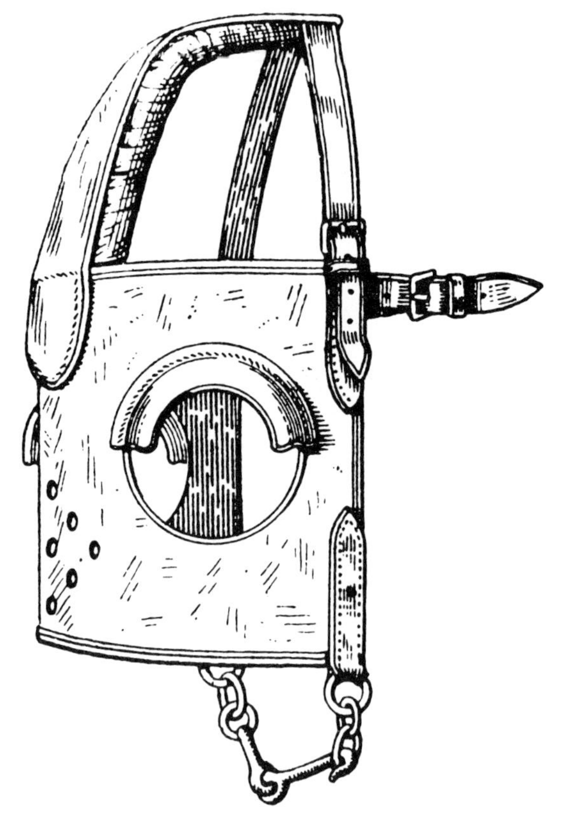

33 'An Improved Head-gear for Pit Horses', submitted by George J. Binns to the Federated Institution of Mining Engineers in 1892. The improvement was claimed to be in the extra protection for the eye given by the circular leather guard.

Harness used to be mended by a separate firm – they collected it from the collieries in a cart. Then they set up a saddler of their own, Shipley's did, and

34 Pony at Blaencuffin mine in 1974. An unusual feature is the helmet lamp on the pony, making a come-back after having been abandoned after unsuccessful experiments in the 1930s.

it all used to go to him; lorries used to take it back and forth. You'd have a load of harness every week, a big heap, broken straps, collars wanting lining, relining, and so on, but they always had to be kept in good order. It was up to the horsekeeper, because if there was any trouble, the horsekeeper got it.

The situation a century earlier is recalled in a letter written on 2 September 1827 by William Henderson to John Buddle, Esq.:

Sir,
As thair is no sadler at North Hetton
Collery I have been advised by Mr. Clark to
Solliset you to have the goodness to give me
A letter to Mr. Morris which I will humblely
Thank you for as it may be the means of gitting
Me the situation I will ask no more then what
I had on Hebburn Colliery which was 15ˢ pr week
I have been 9½ years hear five years I had 18ˢ pr week but
When they reduced the Wadges thay took 3ˢ a week of me
And so it continued ever since I will call on you
Either in Wednesday or Thursday for noon
I have been working at Mr. Lashes factory for a month past
And will be done at the time if you are not at home
I will thank you to leave a letter for me wen I call
Will ever Oblege Your Obᵈᵗ. Humble Sarvᵗ.
William Henderson.

The harness permitted the pony to be tackled up with either shafts or chains. In this it was not unusual, for farmwork above ground also employed both shafts and chains to enable horses to pull a variety of equipment. A cart, for instance, was pulled by shafts, but a plough by chains. Each method has advantages and disadvantages; shafts give a 'direct drive', and allow reversing and braking, but restrict the movement of the horse round the implement, chains are more flexible but can only be used for pulling forwards. Although both systems were used

An Appeal from a Pit Pony.

"More is wrought for want of thought than for want of deed."

To all who are interested in me;—Drivers, Putters, etc.:—

BAD YOKING in the mines is the cause of endless laming and bruising, loss of work resulting from same. A few suggestions what not to do will benefit the many of my underground companions.

DON'T YOKE HIGH in the back this puts the weight of load on my back causing bruises.

DON'T YOKE LOW in the back, this puts the weight of load on my belly, causing bruises.

DON'T YOKE bearing chains tight. These are only to keep empty limbers up off my heels; not to pull with.

DON'T LOOSE neck collar strap to put water bottles on at stables, as you don't fasten after taking bottle off, causing pain all day and a bruised shoulder.

DON'T PULL my throat-band tight when putting bridle on, it is very painful The belly-band also only needs a gentle pull up

PLEASE YOKE ME LIKE THIS

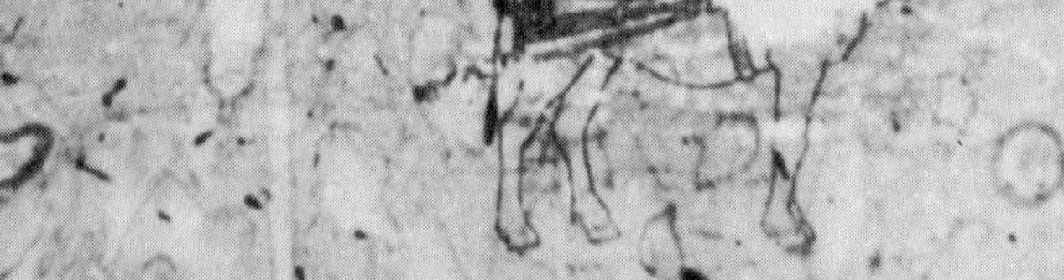

I will then have freedom to do my work with proper control.

DON'T OVERLOAD—it is serious to me and has caused endless fatal injuries.

DON'T FORGET to look in my cistern and food-box. If supply is wanted inform trolleywayman, deputy, or any official. "Thank you."

There are many other things which can be done to assist me, such as a glut-out. Please see to this as crossings, switches, etc., are dangerous traps without them.

"IT IS NEVER TOO-LATE TO MEND" So with this HUMANE APPEAL I am looking forward to remedies in which your kind interest will greatly help the many thousands of such as myself.

JACK.

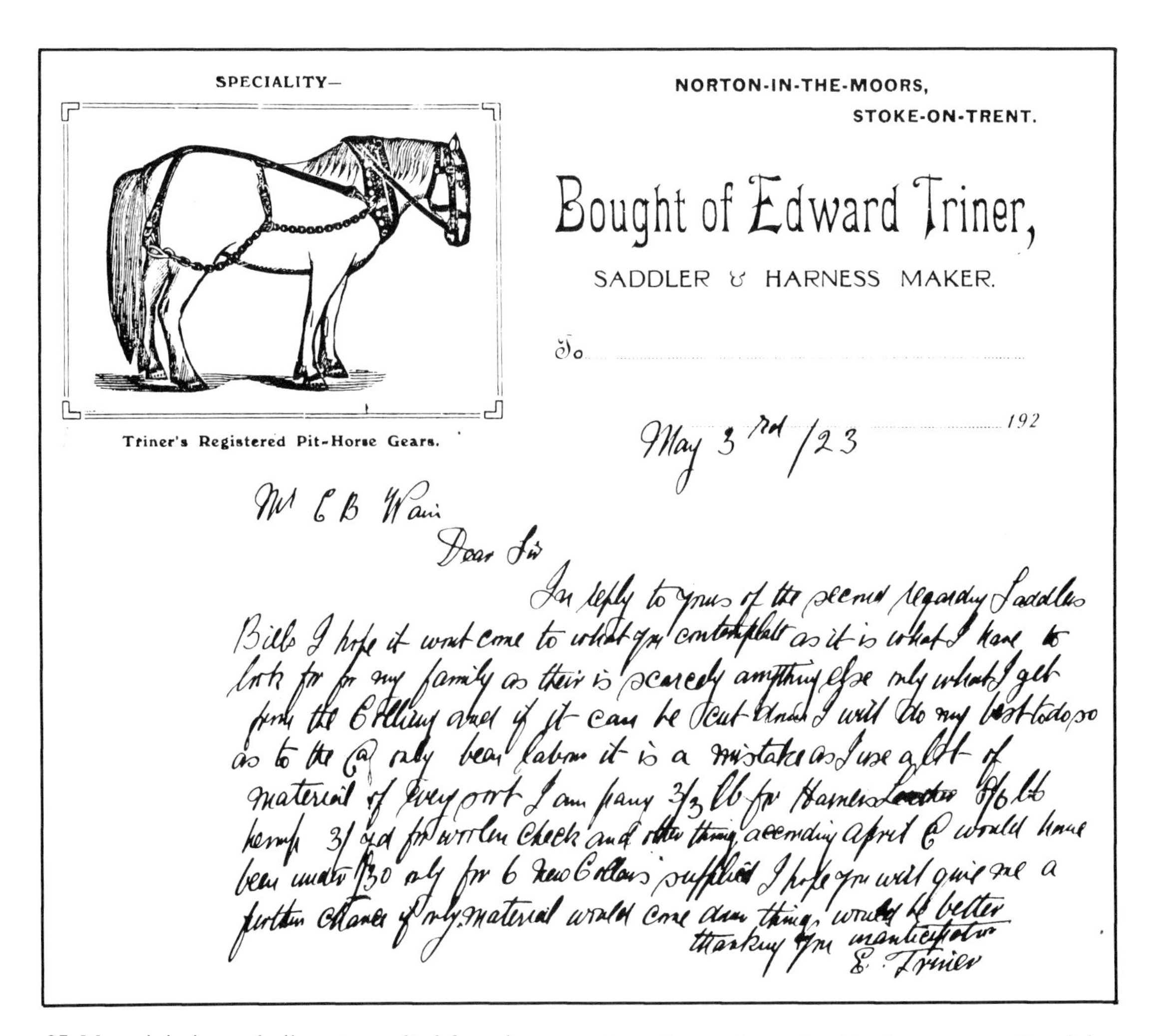

SPECIALITY—

Triner's Registered Pit-Horse Gears.

NORTON-IN-THE-MOORS,
STOKE-ON-TRENT.

Bought of Edward Triner,

SADDLER & HARNESS MAKER.

To ....

May 3rd/23 192

Mr C B Wain

Dear Sir

In reply to yours of the second regarding Saddlers Bills I hope it wont come to what you contemplate as it is what I have to look for for my family as their is scarcely anything else only what I get from the Colliery and if it can be cut down I will do my best to do so as to the @ only bean labour it is a mistake as I use a lot of material of every sort I am paying 3/3 lb for Harness Leather 8/6 lb hemp 3/ 2d for woollen check and other things according april @ would have been under £30 only for 6 new Collars supplied I hope you will give me a further chance if only material would come down things would be better

thanking you manufacturer

E. Triner

35 Many injuries and ailments resulted from horses being badly harnessed or 'yoked', even after the 1911 Act which prohibited horses being worked in ill-fitting or ill-fitted harness. It was hoped that this poster might help drivers to do the job better.

36 This letter is in reply to one from the Manager of Chatterley-Whitfield Collieries Ltd., saying, 'I have been looking into the cost of saddlery work, which keeps very high and which I see whether there is much or little always seems to work out at about the same figure (£40) per month. As by far the greater part of this amount is for labour, it looks as if it would pay us very well to have our own saddlery shop and labour at the colliery.' This, the manager believed, would also have the effect of saving all the trouble with carriage, and he felt it only right to inform Mr Triner what he had in mind, as Triner had done the work for so long. The saddler's pathetic reply is clear indication of the difficulties of the time, and the dependence of some local tradesmen upon the mining industry.

below ground the major difference from normal practice was that the shafts, instead of being part of the vehicle, as on a cart, were attached to the horse, which carried them from wagon to wagon. The shafts were called by the miners 'limbers' or 'limmers', and the use of chains underground was known as 'tracing'.

Limbers were made of either wood or steel. At some collieries they were blacksmith-made or altered to fit individual ponies, and the shaft-irons adjusted to suit the height of the animal. two main varieties of limbers were used, 'loose' limbers and 'fast' limbers. Loose ones required

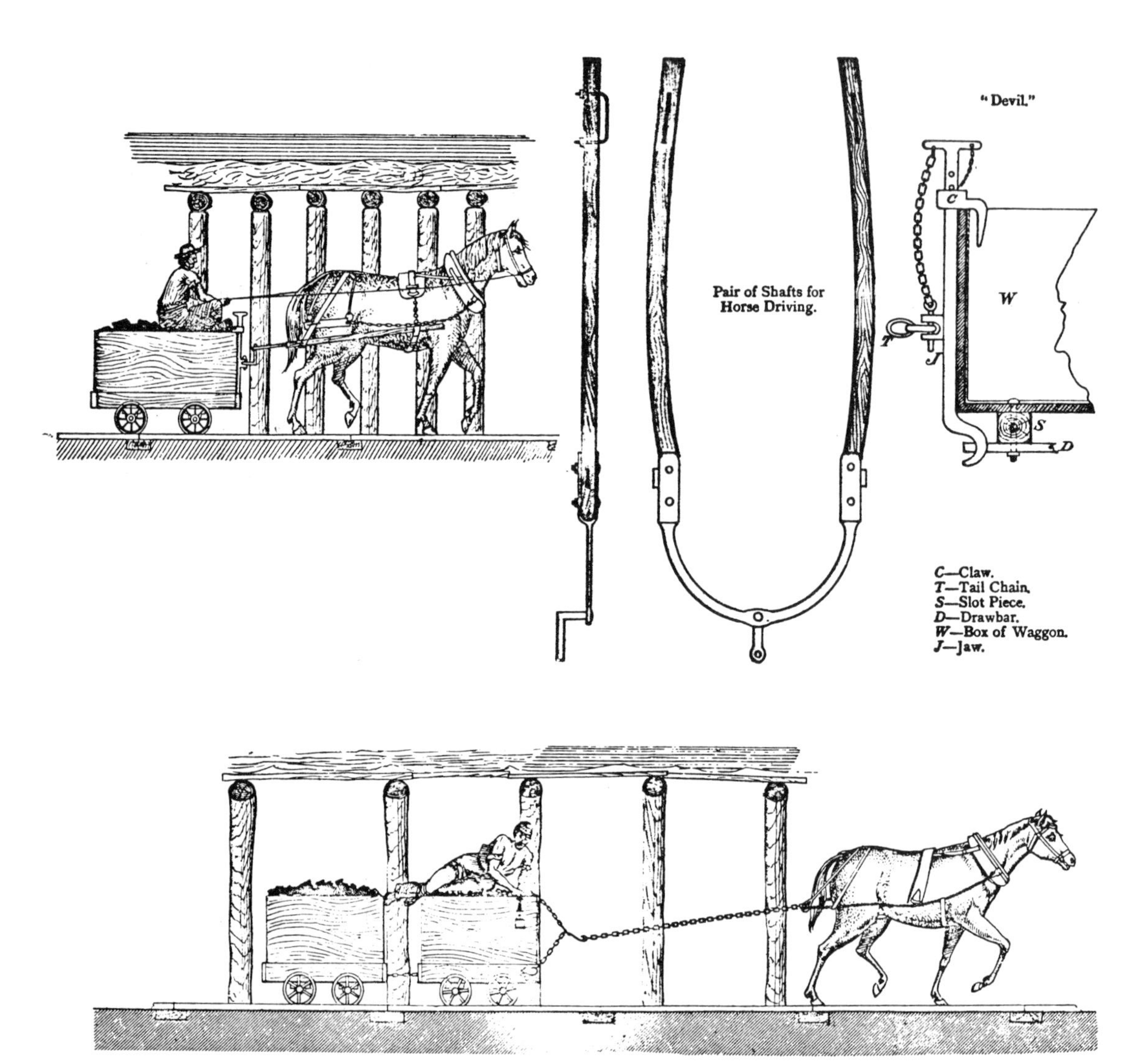

37 A comparison of 'shaft' or 'limber' gear and 'chain' or 'trace' gear. From a mining textbook of 1892.

an extra piece of equipment to connect the limbers to the tub. This 'limber iron', 'gun' or 'shaft iron' was attached to the limbers by the 'nipper peg' or 'gun-pin' – of which the driver normally carried a spare – and to the tub by a cotter-pin or 'shackle-pin'. The fast limbers had this piece welded to the bow of the shafts so that only one coupling to the tub was needed.

A major disadvantage of the limbers was the likelihood of the shaft ends being caught in the timbers of the roadways, which could be very dangerous if it dislodged roof supports. Ponies were also vulnerable when pushed by their load into stationary wagons, as their chests were unprotected. To overcome both these problems an enterprising colliery at Pontefract used shafts which were joined at the front as well as the back of the pony. A miner recalls:

I once saw a runaway pony with two full tubs come tearing into a loading point and crash into a row of full tubs standing on the same track. His circular shafts saved him from being crushed and the only damage was some busted harness and a slightly cut lip.

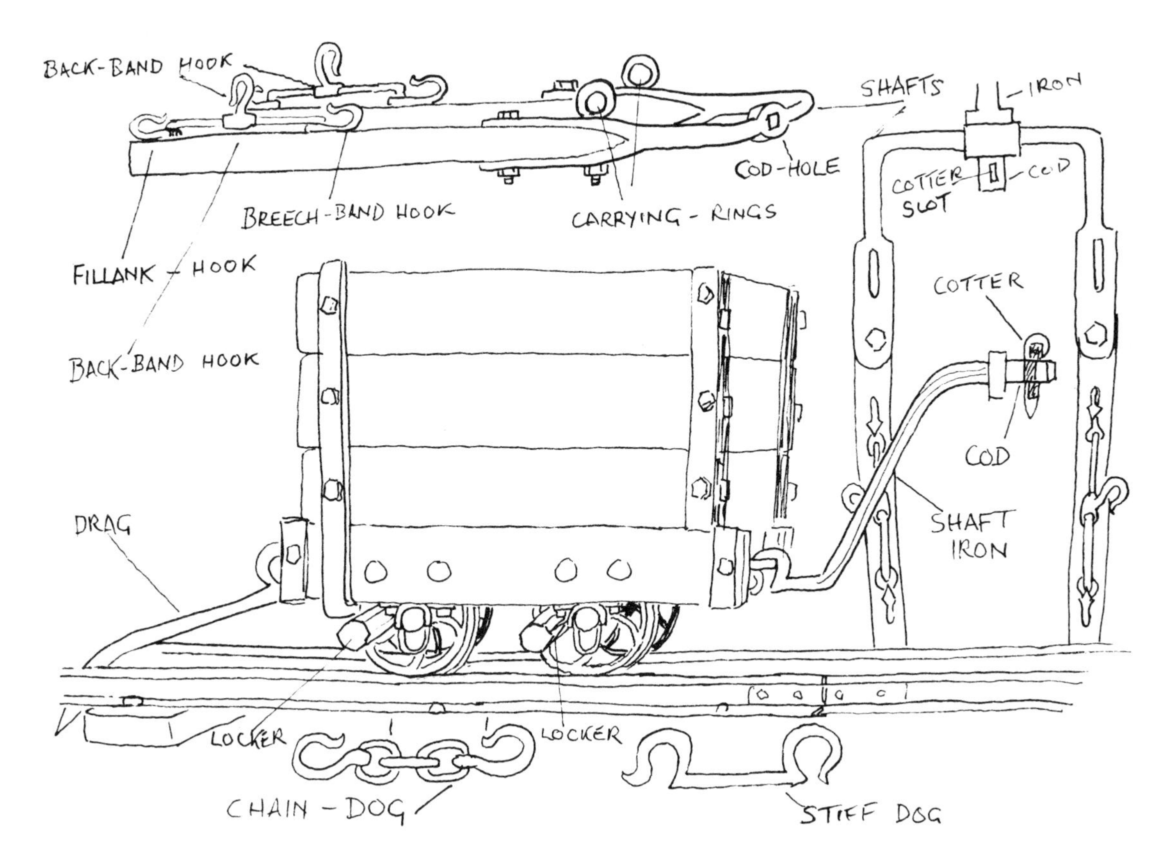

38 A Midland version of 'loose' limbers and tub. Note how the fillank-hook on the limbers takes the strain when the horse is pulling and the breech-band hook takes it when 'braking' or backing. On the tub the drag is there to prevent the tub running backwards down an incline, and the lockers, shown in place in the wheels, act as a brake and are intended to prevent loaded tubs on a downhill gradient forcing the pony forward too quickly.

These 'circular limbers' were harnessed up by leading the pony to stand inside them and the shafts were then raised and hooked on. The 'U' shaped limbers could also be attached this way, but it was easier to stand them up behind the pony, fasten the back chains, and then swing the limbers up to make the other attachments.

Chain gear, sling gear or tail-chains usually consisted of two chains which were hooked onto the collar and then passed down either side to a rod or bar known as a 'spreader' which kept them apart behind the animal. From the centre of the spreader a further chain ran to a 'D-link' which was attached to the object to be pulled,

In some collieries chain-gear was used so infrequently that it was stored back in the stables, whereas the limbers would be kept near the place of work. Such pits used the chains mainly for salvage and rescue work, as the chain allowed the pony, for example, to be further away from a tub caught in a fall of stone, and therefore in less danger of being harmed by rocks falling from the roof as the pony moved the tub. In Staffordshire, though, chain tackle was used more frequently than limbers in the 1930s, for according to the Transcripts of the Institute of Mining Engineers, 91% of all horses there used tail-chain and spreader, but this was exceptional. In mines in general limbers were the rule.

6 Life Underground - Horsekeepers and Feeding, Farriers

The overall responsibility for the well-being of ponies underground lay with the men who were known variously as 'horsekeepers', 'ostlers', 'hostlers', 'horse attendants' or 'horsetenters'. In the larger collieries a number of horsekeepers would be supervised by a head-horsekeeper. Feeding, bedding and surveillance were the main routine jobs of the horsekeepers, but they were usually expected, and prepared, to have a go at anything that arose in connection with their charges.

In decisions concerning a pony's fitness for work, either on a particular day or in the longer term, the horsekeeper's word could only be countermanded by the management, usually through the vet. In some pits the whole responsibility for the decision was put onto the shoulders of the horsekeepers, and this could make life very difficult:

It was the horsekeeper's job to declare that a horse was worked out, not the vet's. So you can see why the ponies were worked until they couldn't stand. If a horsekeeper had stated that a horse couldn't work, while it could still walk, the management or agent would have sacked him on the spot, and jobs were short in those days.

A horsekeeper's life was not an easy one in normal circumstances. Witness two accounts, one from an ex-horsekeeper in County Durham and the second from an ex-head-horsekeeper from Derbyshire:

It was a bit of a naughty job. You had to get up for three o'clock in the morning – you know, to go down with the deputies at three o'clock, get these ponies watered and fed and all harnessed up for the lads coming in at four. Then you went home at eight o'clock, then back again at three in the afternoon. You were there till six, till the ponies came in and you got them bedded down. On Sunday mornings you went down at five and you came back at eight.

I used to go twice a day. 5 a.m., come up at 8.30 – used to come home and have my breakfast, then go on again about 2 till 5 or 5.30. Every day. Sundays I used to go six in the moring till twelve, just one do, you see. Then there was a night man went in each night to see 'em. You worked six days a week till you went in charge, as head-horsekeeper, then you had to do seven. Somebody had to be there.

Somebody always had to be available. Machines can be left standing, animals cannot. Even during the strikes the head-horsekeeper was likely to be the only man, other than safety-staff, allowed to continue to work, looking after the ponies. Generally speaking it does seem that the horsekeepers were fairly conscientious in their care of the horses and many were genuinely fond of them: '*they did everything in their power to make the ponies' lives as easy as possible*'. Routine tasks kept them busy, '*grooming, washing, feeding, mucking out, sweeping the floors and replacing the sawdust, "dressing" the pony so that the ganger had only to fit the bridle and unbuckle the manger collar before taking him out*'. On top of this the horsekeepers in some collieries were required to do such jobs as simple saddlery repairs, the clipping of manes and tails and veterinary attention. The place of the vet in the pit pony world will be considered in the next chapter, but it is certain that many colliery managements saw the employment of the services of a qualified vet as an unnecessary expense, so that completely untrained horsekeepers were often forced into giving first aid and even more permanent treatment and surgery. *'I don't ever remember a vet being required, but any illness or slight injury to a pony was dealt with by the horsekeeper.'* A retired ostler recalls:

I used to stitch 'em. Never thought of sending for a vet. They come for me one night – they sent a little chap, it didn't matter if I wasn't in, he'd got to find me – and I'd gone to the cottage garden. He found me. 'You've got to come' he said, 'for there's a pony wants stitching bad.' And I went. I put him sixteen stitches in his belly, he'd ripped him on something, it were terrible, but I stitched him up. I just used to do ordinary stitching. I hadn't any proper training.'

In order to put this into perspective it should be realised that until fairly recently many farmers only sent for a vet as a very last resort and would attempt to deal themselves with all but the most serious cases of illness and injury to their animals, including their horses.

The horsekeeper normally had to make a daily report to the management on the condition of the horses in his care, and this became formalised after Nationalisation into M & Q (Mining and Quarrying) Form No. 265, which had spaces for the name or number of each horse, the times it left and was returned to the stable, the name of the driver and the horse's condition on its return. If a horse was away from the stable for more than 8 hours in 24 the details had to be entered on another form. No. 265A. The horsekeepers were thus, if they were conscientious, required to inspect each horse as it came back from work each day – many would do this anyway, but the regulations attempted to ensure that all horses were checked every day.

In an article on underground stables, written in 1901, a mining engineer discussed the importance of finding the right sort of horsekeeper. He declared that

'it was desirable to obtain the services of a countryman with a knowledge of horses' but that *'horsekeepers were frequently labourers who knew little of the requirements of a stable and were not trained in stable management, with the consequences that the horses in some mines were neglected'.*

Twentieth century horsekeepers certainly seem to have been either injured or aged miners put into the stables as a light job, usually without any training, or the countrymen that the engineer wanted. A Derbyshire ex-ostler explained how he came to work with ponies:

Well, I'd been in it all my life, brought up on farms. I'd been working on farms, among 'osses just the same as you do down the pit, I were used to that sort of thing. I applied for the job. I wasn't a miner. I took to it right away – though I got the wind up a bit when I started going down in the chair!

The ideal, of course, was both a knowledge of horses and a knowledge of mining, and, as coalmines are usually in the countryside, a miner with a 'hobby' interest in horses was not unusual. Nor was a family interest in pit ponies – a number of miners recalled horsekeepers being followed in the job by their sons and one instance was quoted of three generations becoming ostler at the same colliery, the Newton family at Langwith.

On the lighter side it is interesting to note that the many tasks they had to perform did not stop some horsekeepers finding time to make a bit of money on the side. A Nottinghamshire miner remembered how

the ostlers did the clipping of the horses – and the lads! All the pony drivers had their hair cut in the stables at the pit bottom. They got short back and sides like the army – you knew who were pony drivers by their haircut!

A Northern vet told how he supplied a colliery with white liniment for the ponies and then heard that the horsekeeper was selling it cheaply to the men for their own use, so the vet added oil of chlorastheda, normally used for horse blisters, to the liniment, and the blackmarket sales soon ceased!

Feeding and grooming

The main areas of work for the horsekeepers

39 Easington Colliery. The pony in the second stall ('Colonel') is probably a new pony still 'on trial' as it still has a long tail.

were in feeding and grooming. It was in the collieries' interest that the animals should be well cared for and well fed, and the evidence points to this usually being the case. Of course in this, as in all aspects of the ponies' lives, there were exceptions and some did not get the grooming and feeding that they deserved, particularly if they had to work a double shift, when there would be no time to be cleaned between the shifts and their feeding would be rushed.

The ponies often finished their shift in a filthy state – '*Black with sweat and dust they all looked the same colour, it was quite a job to recognise your own pony on accasions.*' The normal practice was to wash the legs and belly of the ponies when they arrived back at the stables and for the rest of the animals' bodies to be brushed clean. This also allowed the horsekeeper to check the ponies for any injury or harness sores. Many stables had a 'washing stall' equipped with a hosepipe; others had a form of trough through which the horses would be walked. A Welbeck miner tells of the installation of a shallow bath which was filled with Jeyes Fluid, in which many of the ponies would roll and so obtain an invigorating bath! It is interesting to note also that at the modern Ellington Colliery the only hot water underground is that heated in a special low voltage kettle, kept in the horsekeeper's room for the first-aid treatment of ponies' ailments discovered during the inspection.

In considering the grooming of pit ponies it must be remembered that because of the heat and dirt their manes and tails were trimmed very short and the ponies were often 'clipped out', that is, all the coat was clipped to a minimal length. This meant that the job of grooming the individual animal would not take as long as an unclipped horse with a full mane, tail and coat. It was not unknown for a lad who had worked a full shift with a pony to stay on and groom it himself.

The boys often contributed voluntarily to their pony's diet, too. The folklore of the mines is rich with tales concerning tit-bits brought for the ponies.

I would start out in the morning with my snap and bottle, plus anything that I could find for Punch, bread, apples and fresh grass. Taking him down the workings he would walk at the back of me for a short distance, then stop dead, and I'd have to give him a tit-bit. This happened three times each morning and always at the same places.

I took a spare bottle – an ex-army tin bottle called a tin-Dud or Dudley – full of sweet tea, and at snap-time I would give this to Sandy who would take it in his teeth by the neck and up-end it to drink the tea.

Dandy loved sweets, especially Nuttall's Mintoes. A miner left a bag in his pocket when his jacket was hung up, and Dandy crunched them up to pulp still inside the pocket and sucked it through the material.

Many, perhaps most, miners took in treats for the ponies, from specially prepared sandwiches to sweets and fruit and, very frequently, handfuls of fresh grass pulled up from the roadside and stuffed into a pocket on the way to work. These treats supplemented a diet which, in both content and amount, was very carefully worked out by the management. In the 19th century, as soon as ponies were employed in large numbers underground, their feeding became an important element in the running of the colliery. The aim was to find a diet which would keep the ponies in the best working condition at least cost to the company. Selection, proportion, amounts, costs, were grave concerns of the Mining Institutes, who frequently debated the efficient and economic feeding of the ponies. They wanted to provide the animals with nutritious food, but concentrated nutrient needs bulk food to balance it; they wanted to use cheap foods like maize rather than more expensive foods like oats; they wanted to know the comparative needs in dry matter of a Shetland and a 16 h.h. horse.

Towards the end of the 1800s the following proportions were being suggested as a balanced, economic feed for colliery animals:

35–40% chopped hay
17–25% oats
9–12% pulse
17–35% maize

or, as an alternative because oats were dear and maize cheap:

29% hay
12% peas
4% beans
55% maize

The feeding of the ponies at Bedlington Colliery over 20 years was analysed and it was discovered that the feed was divided:

31.2% hay
36.6% maize
5.4% peas
18.5% oats
7.7% beans
0.6% barley

These basic constituents were used in varying proportions according to local availability and price well into the 20th century. Colliery companies with their own estates were able to provide their own hay and grow their own cereals and pulses more economically as well as add such variations as clover during the summer months. Control of their own production also lessened the chances of the feeding of poor quality or even dangerous provender – at Hamstead Colliery in 1894, for example, 12 horses died of Lathyrus Sativus poisoning from the seeds of vetch which came into the stables among peas which were being used in the feed because oats and beans were too highly priced.

The Institute of Mining Engineers was still discussing feed in 1941, only this time because of war-time problems. Now, though, they were considering the merits of pony-nuts and silage, straw-pulp and grass from ungrazed areas like railway embankments. The last few pit ponies are being fed on pony-nuts and hay, with a bran mash once a week. An interesting aspect of this diet is that the hay is fed 'long', that is, as it comes from the bale, and not 'chopped'. Traditionally hay fed to pit ponies has been chopped up small; pit-pony food is consistently referred to by ex-miners as 'choppy', for the feed they recall was a mixture dominated by chopped hay. Why hay was chopped is not certain, but it is more likely to be for ease of handling and transport than for any reason concerning its acceptability to the ponies, or ease of digestion. The mixture reached the stables ready prepared and was shared out into the stalls by the horsekeeper or his stable assistants. Obviously a mixture containing long hay would be impractical, and a mixture of the other ingredients, with the long hay fed separately, would be much more trouble. It is significant that the long hay has only been fed since the number of ponies fell to very few.

Large mining companies would have one central food-store or granary from which the feedstuffs would be delivered to the different collieries. *The Colliery Guardian* reported in 1931 that '*Automatic provender-mixing plants have been installed in a large number of collieries, mixing food for many thousands of ponies. The food after mixing is usually carried in bags to the stables.*' Thus the horsekeepers had only to distribute the feed to the horses and the only inconvenience in this is that, as horses are not ruminants (they don't chew the cud like cows and sheep), they need, ideally, a little food often, not a large amount once or twice a day. As the ponies were also away from the stables for the length of their shift, provision therefore had to be made for them to be fed and watered at their place of work. This meant that food and water had to be taken regularly up into the districts and this, according to many miners, was often not done conscientiously by the stable staff. The choppy-boxes or chaff-bins and the water-butts were usually situated at a collecting place for tubs, the theory being that it was there that a pony would get a brief rest whilst waiting for its next load and so could have a short feed and water if it wished. In practice, however, the choppy-boxes were frequently empty because the men responsible were not filling them daily as they were supposed to do, or the food was wet or filthy or contaminated by mice, rats or cockroaches, and the water-butts were similarly unusable. Often, though, the condition of the provender was irrelevant, for if the putter was behindhand and rushed, the pony was not given time to eat. If the conditions were excessively dusty it was considered a waste of time to put out water as it became dirty so quickly, so the ponies would work all the shift without a drink – though the men, who had only their pint 'bottles', were known to share it with their horses.

In Wales a different system of in-shift feeding was used and seems such an improvement that it is surprising that it was not adopted elsewhere, particularly as it was so common aboveground: '*Each pony had a feed-bag. The bag was filled at the start of the shift and was carried by the pony around the neck. The pony would have his food and water at the same time as the haulier.*' Even this system was not fool-proof, for some hauliers left the bag hanging from the pony's neck all the shift, instead of removing it when the pony was working, and much of the feed was lost through spillage.

There can be little doubt, despite the wholesale condemnation by miners of the refreshment conditions at the work-places, that the pit ponies were, overall, very well fed in most pits. It made sense that this should be so, for a strong, satisfied pony does more work than a weak and hungry one. The economic aspects of pit ponies' work should not be lost sight of, for they were calculated in great detail and affected every aspect of the ponies' lives. To conclude this section on food and care, and to demonstrate the kind of detail entered into, here are two examples of costing. The first, quoted from H.W. Hughes **Textbook of Coalmining**, is answering the question 'How much does it cost a company to keep one horse?' It refers to a colliery where 80 15 h.h. horses were used for 'main road' haulage underground:

Taking the average of many years the total cost incurred for each horse per week is as follows:

	s.	*d.*
Keep	*10*	*2.891*
Repairs to Harness	*0*	*2.538*
2 men at surface, cutting and preparing of feed	*0*	*5.296*
Ostlers (2 men below each of two shifts)	*1*	*9.153*
Brushes and currycombs	*0*	*0.228*
Vet and medicine	*0*	*3.058*
Shoeing	*0*	*6.000*
	13s.	*5.164d.*

In an Institute's records two engineers, Messrs Forster and Simpson, surveyed 12 collieries in the North of England to discover the really crucial figure – the cost per ton of coal of haulage by horses. Here is part of their findings:

Average 27 tons per day led 180 yard by each pony (putting)

Average 30 tons per day led 423 yards by each horse/pony (driving)

in good conditions for haulage average cost for 603 yards – 3.385d. per ton

Farriers and shoeing

In the horse world at large the saying 'No foot, no hoss' is recognised as containing a lot of truth. No matter how well a horse is bred, stabled and fed, if it's feet are not looked after it will not be able to perform to its full potential. Horse's hooves grow in length and need to be trimmed back from time to time, but they are also soft enough to wear away if the animal walks frequently on hard surfaces, and so working horses are normally shod with metal shoes to prevent the hoof walls wearing and the feet becoming tender. The iron shoes are best fitted hot – the heat of the metal is used to burn an accurately fitting bed for the shoe onto the hoof – but cold-fitting can be done by filing the hoof to fit a pre-shaped shoe. It is desirable that the shoeing should be done by an experienced farrier, that is a man who has the metal-working skills of a blacksmith, in order to make the shoes well, but who also has an understanding of horses and specific knowledge of their legs and feet, to enable him to put on the shoes and to care for the feet.

All pit ponies are shod. Open fires are obviously highly dangerous underground and so forbidden, so the shoeing of pit ponies has always been done cold, with the shoes being pre-fabricated in the blacksmith's shop in the colliery yard. After the mines were nationalised the Coal Board included horse-shoeing in their training for colliery blacksmiths and those trainees who showed an ability in the work and a liking for it were able to specialise in farriery, serving either a large colliery or a group of smaller ones. Where no blacksmiths inclined to horse-work, farriers were employed from outside the mining industry. Both these situations were an improvement on what had existed in many of the private collieries, where the standard practice was either for the blacksmith – that is, a specialist worker in iron and steel – to go below ground and fit the shoes as overtime, after a shift doing the normal work in the smithy, or for the horsekeeper to be responsible for the shoeing. In neither of these cases was there any training for the job, or much knowledge other than that picked up in practice.

At its worst this lack of knowledge could lead to loss of efficiency in the pony work-force, to say nothing of the discomfort and even malformation caused to the ponies themselves. A Yorkshire miner described the results:

The shoes all came down cold and were fitted by the horsekeeper. I think this was a mistake, because

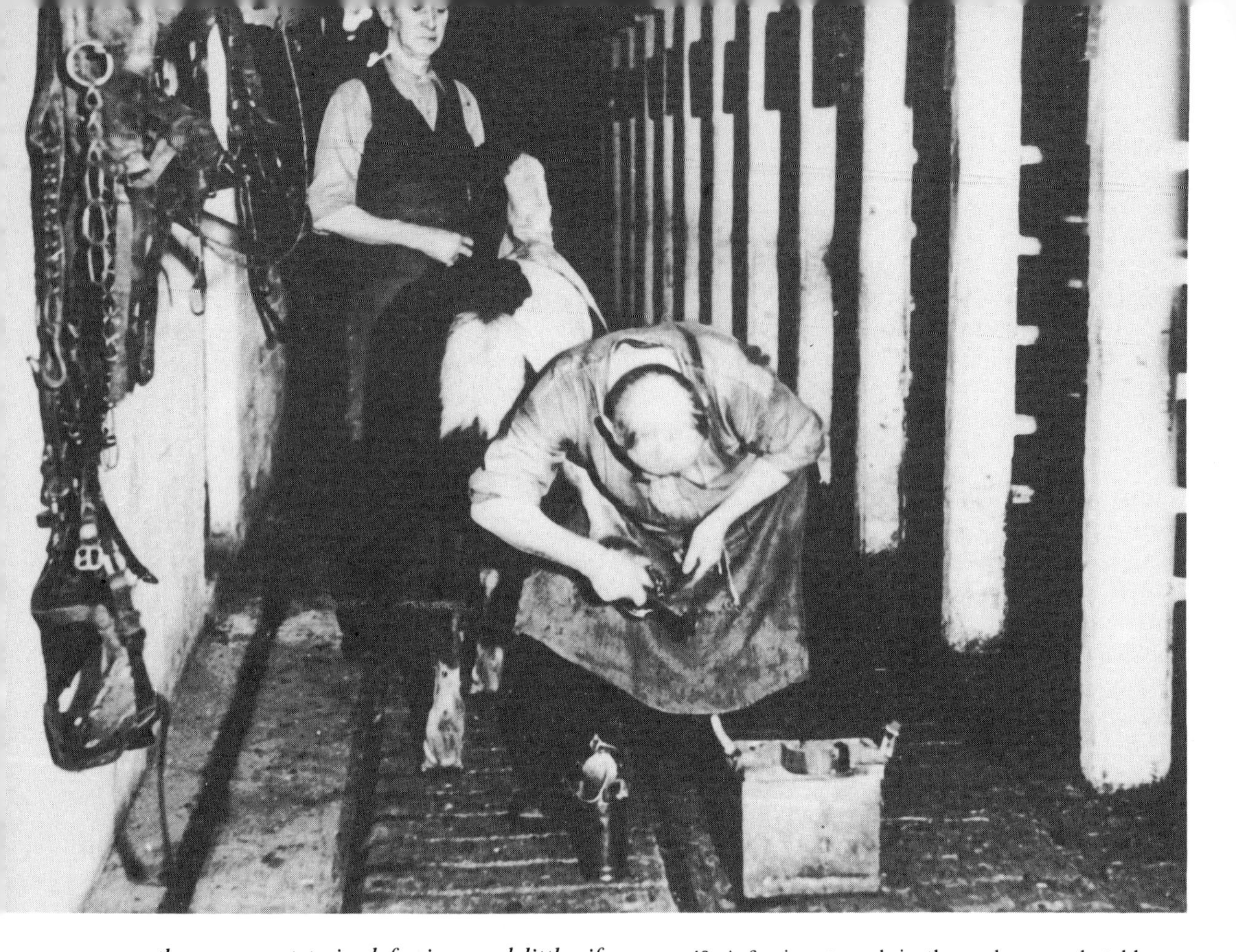

they were not trained farriers, and little, if any, trimming of the hooves was done. Some of them got very long, until the horse no longer stood on his hoof, which grew out, more like a cow's foot.

Another miner is critical of a similar situation:

They were cold-shod underground and especially the older ponies who rarely went to the surface and saw a farrier, used to grow very long hooves, so long that it would throw them back on their heels when walking. It would not have been much of a job to send a farrier down to cut them back to a proper length and stand the pony up on his feet again.

Most managements, though, were aware of the effect poor shoeing could have on a pony's work and were prepared to do something about it either by ensuring that the blacksmiths did receive some instruction and supervised

40 A farrier at work in the underground stables.

experience, or by employing a qualified farrier. This took an unwelcome responsibility off the shoulders of the horsekeepers:

We got a shoeing-smith down the colliery every day. I didn't have to bother about shoes. If I'd got a pony with shoes off he didn't go out to work and I'd put up a board, for when I'd gone away, saying he mustn't go out – we were very strict on that.

The problem for managers was occupying a farrier during the time that the ponies were out of the stables at work, for the horseshoeing was only done in the stables. The shoes had to be made, of course, and this took up much of a farrier's time. A spare set was made for each pony, ready for when needed, and often kept in the stalls so that whenever a farrier fitted a shoe it meant that the next day he had to make another 'spare'. The farrier's blacksmithing skills were also employed repairing broken tools and harness, chains, etc., and often in the specialised area of sharpening the hewers' picks – '*each coal-face worker had his own "mark" on his pick, and the farrier used to sharpen each pick to individual requirements*'. Some colliery companies owned very large areas of farming land and the colliery farriers were used to shoe the farm horses, too. This was the case at Brancepeth Colliery:

There were two farriers above ground doing nothing but making and fitting shoes. Stable-yard horses, farm horses in the locality – all the farms in this area were owned by Strakers and Love and they used to bring all the farm shires to be shod. And the hunters as well, from Brancepeth. But the farriers went underground, in addition.

A good idea of the working conditions of a colliery farrier between the wars can be gained from the following account:

You did your normal shift 7 till 3 in the blacksmith's shop. You made chains, did welding, made tubs, and so on. During spare time in your shift you made your shoes for the ponies underground. 3 till 6 every day was underground farriering; it was all overtime. Every night every pony's feet had to be checked. You picked up every foot, every night. If the horsekeeper knew any were without shoes he'd tell me. They used to get them fastened in the railway lines and pull the shoes off, and sometimes damage the foot. A lot of ponies used to get plate nails in their hooves, well, they were laid off and another pony had to take their place. I used to put Stockholm Tar on their feet; rake all the poison out then put a Stockholm Tar bar on when you'd got all the pus out of the foot. It didn't happen every day, then you'd get a spate of it. Some of the ponies would come off the foreshift at 11 – they'd be in the stables when I got down at three. By the time you'd finished the fore-shift ponies the backshift would be coming in, and the driver-lads would see them to their stalls, take their harness off, see they were bedded and watered, and then we used to go round and examine every foot. Some stalls were small, where the Shetlands were, and you'd be all hunched up and you'd shoe them down between your ankles. If one danced about you'd fasten his head in one corner and his tail in the other. At surface you could put them in stocks, but there were no stocks underground. If you had to use a twitch you needed a helper. We had to shoe with a naked light, there was no electricity then, no special facilities at all. You took the oil vessel out of your lamp and stuck it on top of your tool box, and you'd shoe in that little light.

Against this stark picture of the difficulties of the farrier underground, crouched in the near dark with a kicking pony, the following sound, but clinically worded, advice from an article in the *Journal of the British Society for Mining Studies* makes an illuminating contrast:

Directions for Shoeing: Never pare the sole or frog, and only cut off enough of the horn at the lower end of the hoof to allow the shoe to bed properly; above all, reduce the weight of the shoe to the lowest possible point and do not employ calkins on either heels or toes. Three nails on the outside and two on the inside are quite enough for the forefeet and they should never be placed near the heels.

7 Life Underground - Health and Safety

Pit ponies in general seem to have been very healthy beasts. Drivers, horsekeepers and vets are in agreement that cases of illness have always been comparatively rare in horses in mines. The fact that horses in a pit were isolated from all others of their kind helped to prevent diseases reaching the ponies in the first place – though new arrivals were always a threat – but their way of life meant that any infectious disease caught by a pit pony was likely to spread through the underground stable very quickly. It was, therefore, in a company's own interest to have veterinary care always on hand, whatever the legal requirements in this area. A northern vet recalled an instance when an outbreak of strangles, a particularly infectious equine disease which spreads rapidly in the warmth of underground stables, was not treated early enough and the management found itself with insufficient fit ponies to work the colliery and the whole mine had to be closed down for three weeks. Amateur diagnosis could be damaging, too, as on an occasion when a pony was ill and the horsekeeper diagnosed lockjaw and the working of the pit stopped when the men refused to go down on the next shift. It took the combined persuasion of a vet's diagnosis, the pronouncements of the Company's representative and the manager, and the assurance of the local doctor before the men accepted that there was no danger to them in the sick pony.

Serious injury to a pony could happen at any time and the speedy arrival of a vet might save the animal's life and thus save the company money so, for this reason too, a vet attached to the colliery or at least 'on call' was a sensible precaution which only the most reckless collieries ignored.

A typical example of colliery attachment was a vet on the Durham coalfield who was employed by several collieries on a contract basis in the late 1920s. He was responsible for more than two thousand ponies, for which he was on call for veterinary treatments and supplied all medicines and dressings. He tested new ponies for glanders before they went below ground and was responsible for the quarterly inspections and reports on all the ponies, required by the management. In addition to this he was commissioned by several of the collieries to purchase their ponies from the dealers. When the number of ponies involved is considered, it becomes evident that the vet could only be available for major injuries and illnesses, and that much of the routine treatment would, of necessity, have to be carried out by the horsekeepers. Even the quarterly inspections could not have been very thorough – they were usually carried out at the weekend when the ponies were all likely to be in the stables, but at one colliery, with about 400 horses, the vet was allowed only 7 hours for his inspection, which is slightly less than one minute per pony. In the 7 hours he was required to inspect the general condition of the animals, including their sight, and to check the state of the stables and the food and water supply – a busy day.

Some companies and large collieries made the vet's work a little easier by supplying a horse-hospital near the mine. This might be a whitewashed byre with an acre or two of grass attached, or it might be a series of looseboxes equipped with slings and a variety of tethering places, as at Brancepeth Colliery, or a comparatively sophisticated building with an operating theatre and a dispensary, as has been provided by the NCB at Tondu in Glamorgan. In such places the vet could at least see what he was doing and have easy access to his patients.

The illnesses, ailments and unfit conditions which the pit ponies developed from time to time were those common to all horses in all environments, and only a few seem to have been aggravated by the circumstances in which the ponies worked. Respiratory ailments, sometimes resulting in a broken-winded condition, were undoubtedly made worse by the dusty conditions in which some ponies operated. In contrast, very wet working places often gave rise to the unpleasant 'greasy-legs' or 'greasy-heels':

When I was a driver in the Busty seam we had three or four ponies with greasy-legs – the legs of the ponies were swollen from the foot upwards to the first joint. This swelling looked like a lot of small mushrooms. I don't know if they had any special treatment except their feet were always washed in very strong disinfectant before commencing work and at the end of the shift. I remember when I was driving one of these the coal hewers couldn't stand the sight or the smell of the greasy legs.

Extra problems seem to have been created by the salt water in collieries where the workings run under the sea. Ex-miners comment on the sores which the constant exposure to salt water gave the ponies, to such an extent that it made some of the animals very difficult to handle, so sensitive did they become.

The dim light and darkness in which the ponies lived and worked contributed, according to one colliery vet, to there being more instances of cataract in pit ponies than in horses working in the light. If a pony developed cataract to the extent that it could not see properly, then it had to be removed from the pit, for by law no blind pony could work underground. This matter of blind pit ponies is one which is raised every time the subject of horses in mines is discussed by the general public. There is a strongly held myth that all or most pit ponies went blind through working in the dark. Since 1911 it has been illegal to have a blind horse working in a mine, but presumably the law was made to prevent an undesirable practice, which was at the time taking place, from being carried out in the future. It can be argued, therefore, one may reasonably assume, that before 1911 some blind horses were employed in the mines. Their efficiency, compared with sighted ponies must be doubted, even when the mainly dark working conditions are taken into account, and the collieries would not employ animals that did not earn their keep, so it is likely that the number of blind horses was very small even when their presence was not illegal.

So why does the belief in pit ponies being blind persist? The answer may lie in part in the circumstances under which ordinary ponies (that is, those not specially selected for Shows) were ever seen in large numbers by the public. Note the following description:

They had them all up in the 1926 strike, into a big field of grass. Oh boy! I had to cry looking at them. As you would know, they were all blind, and what with the smell of the good air and grass they just went wild, running, kicking, bumping into each other.

The behaviour is not unusual in horses released into a field (see Chapter VIII) but the assumption that the ponies 'were all blind' needs to be compared with the words of a miner also describing what happened in the 1926 strike: '*We had all the ponies up, and it was proper bedlam for 3 or 4 days, because they didn't have their sight back until the end of that time.*' This is supported by the observation of a colliery vet that '*it might take 24 to 48 hours or more to accommodate to the light when brought to the surface.*'

These and other similar comments indicate clearly that the ponies above ground (and so briefly visible to the public) were likely to *appear to be blind* for several days after coming to the surface, because they were not accustomed to the intensity of daylight. Anyone seeing them in such circumstances might well assume them to have defective vision.

A large majority of miners – though not all – subscribe to the view that blind ponies underground are a figment of the public's imagination; let one speak for the rest: '*I never saw a blind pit pony and I've enquired at work and nobody there has ever heard of a working blind pony.*' However, the Clifton Colliery Horse Books (see Appendix I) show conclusively that some horses did go blind whilst working in the mine – in the 50 years of the records the departure of 458 horses from the pit is detailed, and of these 15 were withdrawn because they were discovered either to be blind or to be going blind. It is impossible to say whether or not the blindness was a result of working in the dark, for horses also go blind above ground, particularly in old age, and 6 of the 15 horses mentioned were between 17 and 22 years old. Fifteen horses going blind in 50 years averages out roughly at one every three and a bit years, certainly not enough to support the public suspicion that most pit ponies lost their sight.

The most frequent injuries which the pit ponies suffered seem to fit into three categories – injuries to legs and feet (by far the most common in all horses); injuries caused by ponies banging into some part of the roadway, often the roof; injuries involving machinery.

Pit ponies were particularly vulnerable in the legs because of the unevenness of the roadways and because, in the dark, they were likely to kick into objects, and tread on others, which, had it been light, they would have avoided. More days work seem to have been lost by pit ponies recovering from damaged hooves – the railway lines underground were especial culprits – and strained limbs, than from any other cause.

'Rooving' or 'scrubbing', the rubbing of the back on the low roof, has already been mentioned in connection with the problems of ponies in low passageways near the working coal-face, and was typical of the common minor injury which would be treated by the horse-keeper. More serious, but still common, was the accident in which the pony's head, rather than its back, received the full impact of the collision. Particularly dangerous were the comparatively sharp edges of roofing girders, for these could damage a pony's eyes or cut the head very badly even when a leather helmet or skull-cap was being worn. This kind of accident – known as 'topping' – occured so frequently under some conditions that the ponies' heads never had a chance to heal from one occasion before they were cut again:

Prince, he was away as soon as you pulled the pin out if somebody didn't hold him. He'd go, till he hit a low girder and it used to scalp him, and that scalp never healed. He stunk like a pole-cat, and every time you took off his bonnet you could lift up the flap.

In some mines the most frequent call for the colliery vet was for a 'topping' to be stitched. Cuts and abrasions from the walls were common, too, especially on the haunches where the damage was done when the ponies turned round in the narrow roadways.

On the main roads, where there was more room to move, the most frequent cause of injury to the ponies was the haulage system itself. The moving wire ropes were a constant source of danger, inflicting nasty burns when the ponies came up against them. If horses were held in any way against a rope, or caught between wheel and rope, much more serious injuries could result. One miner recalled a pony falling onto the wire rope and being very badly cut and burned. The experience was so frightening for the pony that, though the wounds healed, the animal thereafter became quite unmanageable and had to be sent to the surface. Another pony, Jeff,

got his foot trapped in a wheelhouse which was set in the ground and its trapdoor was made of several loose planks of wood. One of the planks moved, trapping his foot and the wheel turned with the wire rope and cut his foot right off. He had to be destroyed at once.

It was not just feet that were caught up in the machinery, as the following harrowing tale – fortunately with a happy ending – goes to show:

One day Bouncer got his head entangled with the endless rope on the binder wheel which hauled empties in and full ones out from the shaft bottom. His head went round with the rope and round the binder wheel. They thought he was dead. They rolled an empty over on its side and rolled him into the tub, to be taken out of the pit. Someone wrote on the tub 'Poor old Bouncer'. But when he was at the shaft bottom waiting to go to bank a young lad noticed what was written on the tub and went to have a look at him. While he was looking the pony's head moved. The boy ran to the man in charge at the shaft bottom, shouting 'He's alive. He's alive.' So the man went to look, saw that he was, rolled the tub onto its side and with help pulled him out. They took the bindings off him, got him to his feet, and sent him back in again, a three mile journey'.

Not all ponies were so fortunate. Many died from accidents underground. At some collieries fatal accidents to ponies were not infrequent, at others men worked for years without witnessing or hearing of one. Of course, in major disasters of rockfall, flooding, explosion and fire the ponies suffered with the men, as at Hetton Colliery in the disaster of 1860, to give just one example. The explosion there took the lives of 22 men, 9 horses and 56 ponies. The death of even one pony, particularly a pony that has been a workmate for some time, is likely to stick in the mind of a miner, and many are able to tell of such fatal accidents in considerable detail.

A pony was most vulnerable when pulling full tubs of coal on inclines. The reasons for this have been discussed in connection with the work of the ponies and the accidents in these circumstances are shown to be caused most commonly by a failure of the simple braking systems – the fracture of lockers or dregs meant to stop the tubs from pushing the pony down a slope, or the failure of a driver to put a barhook on the last tub to prevent the train pulling the pony backwards down an uphill incline. A miner described the general situation:

We would help the pony at the top of the hitch by putting wooden dregs in some of the spoke spaces of the wheels to act as a brake. The dregs were about 12 inches long and about 2 inches square. Sometimes the pony could not keep the load in check, so he would panic and criss-cross out over the sides of the road, when the weight behind would be too much for him and knock him down. Many times there was a terrible smash-up, uprights and supports of the roof coming down, and falls of stone. Many ponies I have seen killed this way, and us driver-lads lucky to jump clear.

Here is a specific example of the same theme:

I was walking in front of my pony, Jack, when I became aware of his head nudging my back. He was breeching harder than usual and I guessed that one of the lockers had broken. All would still have been well but as he strove to hold the tubs one of his hooves went on a rail and he began to skate. Then the point of his shoe went into a gap between the rail sections, and the weight of his load threw him over. As luck would have it one of his shafts went behind a sprag that was holding a coal side up and before I could push all five carfles back the pony was dead, strangled.

Another kind of disastrous ending to the same situation is explained by a Notts. miner:

When the tubs over-ran the pony going downhill, then the driver had no time to open the ventilation doors. The only thing he could do – and this sounds unbelievable but it's true – was to lie down at the side of the tub-track and let horse and tubs smash into the door. Sometimes the pony got off with a bang or two if the door smashed, but mostly they broke their necks. The driver had to lie down because there wasn't enough room to stand at the side.

When a horse is frightened its natural tendency is to try to get away from the source of fear as quickly as possible, for this is the way that horses survive in the wild, by fleetness of foot. Domesticated horses retain this reaction, and when frightened, bolt. In the open country a bolting horse may run far enough to satisfy its desire for safety without inflicting any damage on itself or anything else. In the close confines of a coal-mine, in the dark, a horse that bolted was highly unlikely to avoid at the very least injuring itself badly and might even kill itself by running into obstacles; with a frightened pony galloping at full speed, possibly wearing limbers, in an unlit and narrow passageway, disastrous consequences of one sort or another were inevitable, and many animals did die as a direct result of bolting:

Bean worked near the shaft, pulling tubs up a siding away from the cage. He was highly strung, unpredictable and bad-tempered. On this occasion he ran amok and galloped fifty yards down the siding to the shaft, where he skidded on the greasy boards and couldn't stop. The shaft-gates were open as coal-drawing was in operation and the pony fell through and down the shaft and he was killed.

Very often, though, such an incident would end with the animal not dead but so badly injured that it had to be put down. Even this humane act was not without its special problems because the animal was underground, for the regulations governing safety in mines did not allow the use of any implement which would spark or flash. An 'humane killer' which employed a cartridge was therefore banned. Horses might be transported in a tub to the surface, where such a weapon was kept at some collieries, but, if a horse could not be moved without unnecessary distress, other methods had to be found to destroy it. One means employed during the 1930s was described thus:

It was a steel helmet, not unlike a German war helmet, but flatter. It was shaped to fit on the horse's forehead in front of its ears. It was strapped tightly onto the horse's head. On the top of the helmet was a hole. The procedure was to place a steel spike with a flat top into the hole. It was pointed sharp as a needle, and just rested on the pony's head, protruding about six or seven inches out of the helmet. An eight-pound hammer was then used to drive the spike into the horse's brain.

This method may seem crude but it was usually quick and effective in use and certainly an improvement on any of the improvised means which were used in the absence of an approved instrument. In any case, things were improving; the hand-driven spike was obviously not the ultimate in painless killers, and the following information appeared in *The Colliery Guardian:*

The Board of Trade, in pursuance of Clause 2 of the Explosives in Coal Mines (Horse Killers) Order 1931 made under S.61 of the Coal Mines Act 1911 has approved a type of horse-killer known as the 'Exit' human horse-killer, invented by Mr. H.B. Stevens of Etwall, Sutton-in-Ashfield, Notts., for use below ground in all mines to which the Coal Mines Act 1911 applies, subject to certain conditions, one of which is that no explosive shall be used in the appliance except that known as Kynoch's 0.320 calibre blank ammunition loaded with 4 grams of black powder.

To have 'his' pony's life ended by a humane killer was likely to be a traumatic and memorable experience for a young driver. Equally memorable were occasions on which a pony in some way saved the driver from accidental injury or death, or merely helped them out of a difficult situation. Incidents of this kind are recalled with gratitude by ex-drivers, and many close relationships between pony and driver were forged in this way. It is especially interesting how often miners, relating 'rescue stories', attribute the happy outcome to some 'sixth sense' which they believed the pony possessed. Miners' belief that ponies could see in the dark has been referred to briefly in connection with their work underground, and the strength of this belief is seen in the many simple rescue stories which pony drivers are able to tell:

We had oil lamps and they were knocked out very easily, but in complete darkness Bounder would always guide me to safety by my holding onto his tail and it gave me a great sense of security; what a great companion for a young boy.

Bloom had the ability to go on to the shaft-bottom on his own – for example, if my lamp was accidentally knocked out and me being left in the darkness I would get hold of his tail and he would lead me out, a journey over $2\frac{3}{4}$ miles, with my head bent low in case I hit it on some low parts of the roof.

Many more examples could be given, but these two will suffice to link the ponies' ability to see in the dark to the miners' appreciation of the 'sixth sense'. The following story exemplifies the way in which '*the remarkable sixth sense was probably the saviour of many drivers and putters*' when horses were aware of things of which the men were ignorant:

On one occasion Fido and I were travelling towards the coal-face with a run of empties when suddenly and for no reason at all, apparently, Fido stopped. I shouted to him, 'Come on, you black so-and-so.' He answered by snorting loudly through his nostrils. Again I spoke to him, but he declined to move, and snorted again. Then I went back towards him, thinking he wanted to pass urine – I used to whistle to help him. When I got up to him he rubbed his nose on me and snorted again. Seconds later there was a terrific crash and tons of earth and stone fell where I had been standing. Had it not been for Fido's sixth sense warning I would have been buried under that fall.

The obvious explanation for this 'sixth sense' is to attribute it to the ponies' particularly acute senses of smell and hearing. Deprived of full use of sight by the frequent absence of light it is likely that the horses would learn to depend on their other senses, already much more highly developed and more highly tuned than in human beings. It is commonly accepted that some creatures, like bats, use their sensitive hearing system as a form of radar to avoid obstacles and to catch prey in the dark, and it is possible that all animals with highly developed hearing have something of this radar ability to 'see with their ears' to some extent. Thus a pit pony in the dark might collect information as to its whereabouts and the nature of its surroundings by listening to the sounds rebounding from objects, as well as using the smells it can detect in the air. The smells and 'echoes' would be unnoticed by the miners unless they were very pronounced. As one miner explained, after describing how his pony led him out of the darkness: '*I believe he knew his way because he either smelt his stables or he could feel the air getting fresher as he was walking towards the shaft outby.*'

The same would apply to the faint sounds which might fore-warn of a movement in the rock; ponies might hear them when men didn't, giving the impression that some extra sense was at work. But sixth sense or not, the miners certainly learned to trust their ponies' natural abilities, as the next example illustrates:

One time another lad worked Beech on the same district as me and he didn't understand the nature of the work. One place where 150 yards of coal had been taken out the timber had been drawn but it held up for a long while, what is called past-stone. This lad was serving the two men on the coal-face, alongside this vacant lot. I was working on the heading above the two men, when this lad went to hitch the pony to the full tub to draw it out from the hewers. I heard the lad shouting at the pony, so I knew something was wrong. I told him to leave the pony go and called the two men out. We all ran. The 150 yards came down with one thunderous roar. The draught from it blew all our lamps out just as we turned the heading away from it. If it hadn't been for that pony we would have died. He could hear the stone working where men could not. Fortunately I knew the pony and understood there was something wrong when he was acting on.

At other times ponies' unusual behaviour was not interpreted as a danger signal – at first:

One particular day I was driving up the landing having taken the tubs away from the conveyor when halfway up the landing the pony crossed out from between the ways. I pushed him back into the way and he crossed out again. Then all of a sudden there was a fall of stone. He had heard it, but I had not and I should think he saved my life.

Bounder saved my life. He was so willing until one day he stopped pulling the tubs of coal. I was wild with him, talked with him, but it was no use. I couldn't understand him, he had never done that before. Then, suddenly, ahead, there was heavy fall of roof.

Restlessness combined with unusual disobedience and signs of fear in a pony were patterns of behaviour which miners did well to take notice of:

Another man and I were moving between jobs and

41 Accident: the shared dangers of man and pony.

had stopped for our snap. We sat on the ground, the pony standing by, when suddenly the pony started to snort and stamp about. The other chap said, 'We'd better move, he doesn't like this spot.' We had got about 100 yards down the road when the roof caved in. Where we'd been sitting was tons of stone.

Sandy normally stood still without being tethered. One snap-time I sat on the first-aid bench in a lay-by. Sandy moved off a few yards and would not come back when I called, which was unusual. I went to him and he walked further away, until we were about a hundred yards from the lay-by. I thought he was playing up and got hold of his harness intending to scold him, but I noticed that he was trembling all over. I thought he was ill or frightened, so I talked softly and patted him to calm him. As I did so the crashing sound of roof falling came and the road where the lay-by should have been was completely blocked. But for Sandy I might have been under it. I like to think that he waited for me, because he could have gone half a mile clear away.

An honest and revealing phrase in the previous account is 'I like to think that ...', for in those words is a possible explanation of many of the occurrences in these tales. The scepticism of non-miners, on hearing a 'rescue story', is often provoked by the ex-driver attributing human qualities to the pit ponies in order to explain their actions. '*I like to think that ...*' disarms such scepticism, and needs to be read into many of the stories. Here are three 'rescue stories' of a different kind from the ones just quoted. Here the animals behave in a way which the miners 'would like to think that ...' was deliberately intended to protect the driver, and though 'logical' explanations may be offered by the sceptic, no-one can say with any finality who is right and wrong:

Ranji ... saved me from serious injury if not death when I was riding the limbers. We were britching through sludge and water and swiftly descending an incline. Ranji hit the ventilation door with his head to open it and the snatch caused the limber cock to jump from the haulage drawbar and I fell between the tubs and the horse's hooves. Ranji immediately stopped. His solid rump rammed into the tubs (they were already on my legs in the sludge) and held them and there he stood with a ton weight on his rump till assistance arrived. He had apples and taters for a month after, and I never lost a shift!

I was running down a steep hill to turn a rail in order to allow the full tubs to proceed, and as I bent down to turn the 'point' I slipped on a wet sleeper and fell down with Fido and the tubs almost upon me. Obviously realising the tubs would hit me, Fido shoved his back end into the breach and shot his front legs straight out, thus 'throwing' the first tub off the track only inches from where I lay.

I was leading a pony from the coal-face pulling five or six full tubs. The rails were never in good condition and if on a bend the 'fish-plates' holding the rails together were worn we had to push each tub in turn over the bad joint. I was doing this, waiting with my back towards the roof prop to give me extra pushing power, when the pony stumbled on the rail sleepers because the hole had been dug too deep between the sleepers. As a result I was struck in the chest by the steel bow in front of the pony. I don't know how long I lay there, but I was told that when they found me the pony was straddling over me, its legs either side of me and it had never moved. Had the pony done so the tubs would have passed over me. I recall being taken home (not to the hospital) by pony and trap, to await the doctor.

There are suggestions also that ponies developed a kind of 'pit-sense' in the same way that the miners themselves did. This pit-sense was a kind of awareness of what was safe and what was suspect in the work they were required to do, a defensive and a protective instinct which was very valuable in such an aggressive environment. Here is an example of this possible pit-sense:

Jason refused, ever, to go farther than the end of the flat. He would never venture further than this to take the tubs to the coal-face, because there was a very steep hitch followed by twists and turns. I even covered his head with my jacket but he would not go, so he had to be moved to another district. One week later the pony which took his place was killed by a full tub running away on the hitch. I can only think that he sensed the impending disaster.

Ponies could also, it would seem, develop special skills to avoid injury:

I have known ponies who were adept at kicking the cotter out of the shaft-iron if they had to breech too hard when a locker broke. Then of course, the iron acted as a sprag, staking itself against a sleeper, throwing the first tub off the road, thus bringing the train to a halt.

On a lighter note, examples have come to notice of ponies learning, as it were, to 'play the system'. A particularly cheeky example of this involved a pony called Rosie:

There used to be a wire from the end of the loading gate, where the coal went into tubs off the face, right to the face. If Rosie knew you could not find her she pulled the wire and stopped the belt. Someone would check why the belt had stopped, and so find her. If something funny happened where she was, she carried out the same procedure.

The tales quoted in the past few pages have cast the pony in the role of hero and the concentration has been, rightly in a book about pit ponies, on the deeds of the animals. It should not be overlooked, however, that the situation was often reversed and ponies were often rescued by the wit and endeavour of their human companions. Miners have died because they refused to leave a dangerous situation without first rescuing, or attempting to rescue, the ponies they were driving.

42 Redundancy: the underground horses after coming to the surface on the last production day at Ty Trist Colliery, Tredegar, in 1959. The ponies seem, in this poignant photograph, to be as scrap as the abandoned metal and buildings that surround them.

At the other extreme it was not unknown for lads, instead of reporting their ponies' injuries to the horsekeeper, to throw dirt onto sores and cuts in the hope that they would not be noticed, In this way the lads hoped to escape the consequences of any carelessness on their part. Such behaviour brings this consideration of illnesses and accidents back to the continual conflict in the mines between feelings and finance, which money could so often win against man's better nature. All the anecdotes in this chapter, indeed, in this book, have to be seen against a background of that struggle, which is highlighted in stark simplicity in this incident from the 1920s:

One day my father-in-law was driving a pony which went lame towards the end of the shift. When he got back to the stables, taking three times longer than usual, he reported it to the horsekeeper. Next day he was told that the pony was alright, but when he turned it round the pony squealed with pain. He said that he was not taking it out. The horsekeeper said 'Tell the Under-manager,' which he did. The Under-manager said 'Fetch him out and we'll have a look at him.' He hit the pony across its rump with his walking stick and said 'Either take him out, or go home; he's shamming.' So my father-in-law went home. The next day the pony was found to have a three inch strand of wire in its leg, which kept it off work for a week.

End of working life

While a pit pony was earning its keep, doing the work it was purchased to do, it was retained in the mine. Once it ceased to earn its keep, for whatever reason, it was brought out of the pit and disposed of for as much as possible by the most convenient means. This sounds very harsh, and certainly no just reward for a pony which had given of its best during many years in the mine, but the world of the working horse, whether pit pony, farm-horse, tradesman's cart-horse or whatever, was an unsentimental world in which the vast majority of horses which could no longer earn their corn were disposed of.

Ponies which proved unsuitable for work underground at the outset were returned to the dealer for resale into some other work. Any animals unable to cope with pit work because of an injury or illness might also follow that route, though some might be given work which was less arduous, either underground or at the pit-head. Many colliery stables included such an animal, which was retained to do small, light jobs, thus avoiding taking a putting or driving pony off the main work force or subjecting an animal to a double shift.

Sometimes an aged and weakening horse was employed on such jobs – a rare example of sentimentality creeping in – particularly when the old horse had been a favourite of the stable workers. The vast majority of pit ponies which survived into old age were unceremoniously written off in the books as 'Worn Out' or 'Worked Out' and sold at carcase price to the knackerman. Only a very, very few were bought by individuals or societies and given any kind of retirement at grass; until the NCB took over, this was virtually unknown.

Every colliery had its record of ponies that lived and worked below ground well into their 20s, and this was frequently offered as proof of the well-being of the ponies. For many a young horse, though, a fatal accident meant that its final journey from the mine was in a wagon, conveyed to the surface like coal and the most enduring image in the mind of an ex-driver-lad might well be a tub with hooves sticking out.

Pony redundancy

The intention of the NCB to phase out the use of pit ponies by the early 1970s meant that several thousand horses would need bringing to the surface and disposing of in some way. Some would be in very small groups and would be absorbed locally, particularly where the pony redundancies coincided with small colliery closures. Local newspapers of the 1960s and 1970s in the coalfield areas were full of news of 'pony pensioners', often being taken into retirement with the miners and horsekeepers who worked with them. The animal protection societies were very aware of the dangers of simply allowing anyone who wished to do so to adopt a pony or buy one very cheaply. The RSPCA collaborated with the NCB to implement the 1956 Coal and Other Mines (Horses) Regulations to ensure that the older ponies, not fit to be sold for further work of any kind, would only be sent to 'a recognised home or private owner approved by the RSPCA or other animal protection society, or put in a home under Coal Board control.' This meant in effect that anyone offering a home to a retired or redundant pony would receive a visit from a representative of a society who would then complete a report giving details of the facilities offered and the society would advise the NCB of their inspector's recommendation.

The 'agreement' also indicated that working-fit ponies should not be sold to dealers or by auction, as the future of any animals so sold would be out of control of any authority. Even so, the RSPCA and the National Equine Defence League were very concerned lest the redundant ponies should be bought by dealers exporting animals for the foreign horse-meat trade, and the societies created a large amount of publicity in their attempts to protect the ponies. No doubt they were to some extent successful, but neither they, nor the NCB, who admitted that it could not 'undertake responsibility for these ponies for the rest of their lives, whatever happens to them', could ensure that the ponies did not fall into the hands of unscrupulous dealers.

Two examples quoted from miners will serve to illustrate the widely differing fates of the ponies:

When in 1965 the Fair Lady pit, Heath Heys, Cannock Chase, closed there were only six old horses left on the last day. The man in charge said these ponies had to be put down in spite of pleadings by handlers who had been in charge for a number of years and who offered to take these ponies to the surface and care for them. Some of these ponies had been down 26 years. They were put down and left down the pit.

Ant worked for 21 years at Blanaevon Colliery near Pontypool. Then he was kept as a pet at The Three Horseshoes pub in Pentwynmaur, and was also adopted by the local Junior school. He had two meals a day and beer with his meals!

8 Pit Ponies Above Ground

Most underground pit ponies came to the surface only very infrequently, if at all. Individual animals might be brought up for treatment if badly injured or ill, or if they were required for shows, but the whole stable would ascend only during lengthy strikes or if the colliery was one of those which brought them up during the men's annual holiday. Bringing ponies to the surface was never without its difficulties and when the entire equine workforce was involved it became a tricky, time-consuming and expensive operation.

Some collieries had the forethought to begin the action by having the farrier remove all the shoes from the ponies whilst they were still belowground. Elsewhere only the hind shoes were removed and a few pits seem to have omitted even this precaution. The ponies were then brought 'to bank', to the surface. The difficulties experienced in transporting ponies up and down the shaft have already been commented on in Chapter III, to do with the arrival at the pit of a few ponies. What is under consideration here is a much larger operation involving perhaps hundreds of ponies, so it would repay a colliery to make some provision to assist both the men and the horses involved. Perhaps, for example, a temporary modification might be made to the cage to make it more suitable for the animals to be carried in it. This kind of activity was not without its dangers, as at least one colliery learned by experience:

For bringing the ponies up they had a special box, with two sets of wheels, that just fitted into the chair. They'd run it on and then it was fastened into position, pinned. But before that, about 1920, they used to have an iron gate which slotted into the hinges and was closed with a sneck. That was all that was holding the men in as they went up and down. It was bad for the men, but that's how things were – you'd only got to push, and lift up, and the gate was off. Well, on one occasion they shoved a horse on, it was frightened and kicking – you can hear them kicking going up the shaft – and the gate dropped down and the pony fell and was smashed to pieces in the sump, which smelt terrible for a long while. And from then on they made this box of wood, like the ones race-horses use, and it's impossible now for a pony to tumble out.

The ponies were not used to travelling up the shaft and it was no doubt a frightening experience, for the cage moved suddenly and travelled fast. Even getting the ponies onto the cage at all could provide its problems, and the following description will seem familiar to anyone who has tried to box an unwilling horse:

Getting the ponies out of the pit was a work of art. The system was to send them out on the cage one at a time. The cage was equipped with a gate, made of four or five crossed pieces of flat slats of iron and for the ponies these were replaced by stout wooden doors which completely blocked the cage entrances and made them into two large boxes. The horses had to be pushed, pulled and manhandled onto the cage. When the driver in front got into the cage, to pull his horse on, his biggest job was then getting himself off – he had to crawl out under the horse's belly. The door at the back of the horse was put on and all hell broke loose on that cage – the horses would kick the door all the way up the shaft and the echoes boomed like thunder.

For whatever reason, and by whatever method, the ponies were brought to the surface in large

43 Pit ponies in a field at Welbeck, during the 1926 strike. A visit to the ponies became the object of many families' Sunday afternoon walk.

numbers, their arrival at the pit head could create something of a community occasion. As a Derbyshire miner put it:

You'd walk your pony off, through the ventilation doors and out, down pit yard, and it was a sight, because all the children knew and were waiting, hundreds of children, waiting at top of pit lane. Right up to dusk, one at a time, a hundred and twenty ponies. All the children came, and brought carrots and crusts.

This interest of the miners' children could continue throughout the ponies' stay above ground. The drivers, too, would often visit the ponies, and the rare opportunity to allow the family, particularly the womenfolk, into the men's working world, was not missed. Especially during the long strikes the field containing the pit ponies became the objective of family walks so that fathers and sons could show off 'their' ponies to the women and girls.

The reaction of the ponies to their release into the fields was predictably one of violent action: '*It was proper bedlam, they'd run about kicking and squealing*' and '*they seemed to go mad at first.*' The consequences might be serious: '*The ponies were brought up and turned out, they just turned them loose, and there were ponies killed. Killed each other. They were all fit, full of choppy, and never been up, and the kicking and fighting, and the biting, you never saw anything like it, it was chaos.*'

Despite the removal of the shoes a great deal of damage could be done in the first days of a 'holiday', and reports of serious accidents are common. To some miners the cause of this 'madness' was the sudden exposure to the light which could, they believed, temporarily blind the ponies, for hours if not days, the inference being that the animals galloped about in the panic caused by the 'blindness' (a subject discussed in Chapter VII). A more likely explanation is to be found in the behaviour of any horse turned loose into a field after being under close control for a period of time. The first response to the new freedom is frequently a buck or two, a few kicks and a gallop round the field. Instruction manuals of horsemanship invariably stress the prudence of releasing a horse with its back to the open field, so that the handler can more easily avoid the first movements of the horse, which are *expected* to be violent. It is also observable that any loose horses which are strangers to each other will quickly set about establishing a leader and a 'pecking order', and that this will involve a lot of kicking, biting and chasing round the field. The wild behaviour of newly-released pit ponies is likely to be, therefore, a combination of response to the sudden lack of restraint and the establishment of domination in the herd.

Many a miner, though, saw the wild galloping simply as an expression of release and joy, and took delight in witnessing the happiness of his holidaying workmate in its newfound freedom.

They were put into the field just outside the pit yard, and they just loved it. They would gallop round and round the field, just for the joy of it, and all the folk from round about would come to look at them. The drivers would go down and call them by name.

In 1911 a local strike at our pit had the owner turning all the ponies out into the field. It was a surprise to find Punch knew me when I called him. Two or three times each day about fifty or sixty boys would go to the field with their titbits for the horses they loved so well.

But if the ponies were above ground long, they changed. They grew fatter in their unaccustomed idleness, they got wilder with their lack of handling and after a while many tended towards an unwillingness to answer to their names, and even to ignore their visitors.

If there were problems in bringing the ponies up and releasing them, there were even more difficulties in taking them below again:

On the Sunday before the Monday starting most of the local lads, those that lived in the village, well, they called for us to get the ponies in again. But you never could catch them, they'd break away. They had this sixth sense of having to go down again. We had to chase them for fields to get them back again. The farmers were up in arms. There were two ponies broke away and went right up the A1 and we were still out at night time trying to catch them. They just went bloody berzerk, ye knaa.

At another pit:

the lads had to round them up on Sunday evening. They rode the ponies that permitted this, and herded the others. Sometimes the wayward ones would take a fancy to gallop round the streets and for entertainment value it beat any racing hollow.

Even when the ponies were safely below ground again and re-shod the troubles were not over:

Now the fun started. On Monday when we went to fetch the ponies out of the stables we had the job of our lives. All the ponies were full of life after their holiday and we had a job to control them, even to put their harness on, because they'd keep kicking it off. It was at least a week before they settled down.

It was even longer, according to a colliery vet, before the ponies were back to working fitness; there would be a loss of weight and condition as the ponies returned to the hard food after the grass diet and it could take as long as three or four weeks for a full restoration to a pre-holiday state. The putters disliked the natural result of the ponies' unaccustomed grass diet, what the miners called 'grass looseness', the almost liquid droppings of the horses, which could make riding the limmers even more hazardous and unpleasant.

These problems inherent in bringing the ponies up to the surface and then returning them resulted in many collieries either never embarking on a 'holiday' routine, or ceasing to operate it. It was not unknown, either, for the ponies to be kept underground even during long strikes, in which case horsekeepers were permitted by the union to go below ground to look after the ponies. This meant, though, that some arrangement had to be made to exercise the horses, which could not be left standing in their stalls for weeks on end. As many as thirty ponies might be exercised at once, for half an hour a day, attached to a single long rope. A considerable financial advantage in bringing the animals to the surface lay in the minimum of attention they required in the fields, though it should be noticed that some collieries continued to feed them even there.

The animal welfare societies who campaigned for holidays for the ponies did not receive total support from the miners. Some of the drivers saw the disruption of the ponies' routine as both damaging and unkind –

Many people used to say it was a good thing to bring the ponies to bank during holidays and strikes, but in my opinion, to bring them to the surface, to nice fresh grass, then take them back again was cruel. A case of 'What you've never had, you never miss'.

Others were alarmed by the physical damage inflicted upon each other by the ponies – the 'holidays' at one Northumberland pit, for example, were brought to an end specifically by the number of broken legs suffered in one particular year. A major question was whether the trouble and risk was justified by the 'rest' and 'freedom' in the fresh air experienced by the animals. This is another example of human values being presumed to be relevant to beasts. Human beings seem to benefit from a rest from their normal labours and responsibilities, and seek out for their holidays a totally different environment from their working one. The funfairs and crowds of a resort, the luxury of hotel life, the quiet of the the moors or the exploration of foreign lands are all representative of a search for a change during the holiday break. The pit pony emerging from the darkness and toil of the pit to the idleness and sunlight of a field is obviously a close parallel, but can the *benefits* of the change also be equated?

The physical change may have been beneficial to the pony, though even this may be doubted. Vets and horsekeepers have pointed out that the conditions of temperature and humidity belowground are fairly constant; there may be no summer underground, but there is no winter either. Consequently the ponies are unused to climatic changes and exposure to the elements, and rain and wind are as likely experiences in the British climate as sunshine. The change of diet and lack of work affecting the ponies' condition have already been mentioned, and the change back, when the ponies descended again could bring further alterations to fitness and, might be argued, unnecessary stress for the ponies as they tackled their normal workload whilst still in their softened state. It is worth noting, for comparison, that a hunter, after a summer at grass, is gradually hardened up and brought back to fitness by many hours of roadwork and schooling before it is expected to perform as it did before its summer rest; the pit pony was back to work next morning.

It is impossible to discount totally the miners who felt that the ponies experienced pleasure similar to their own when released from their pit labours for a week or two, although obviously nothing of the kind can be proved. The drivers read joy into the cavorting of the horses, and were pleased to find it there, glad that the ponies they worked with could also find some reward in their rest from toil. Some men visited the ponies regularly, and observed their behaviour:

The ponies at Bellington were brought to the surface for the annual holidays. A pony from 'A' pit made friends with a pony from 'B' pit and for the following two weeks they grazed together and nuzzled each other and were never apart, never bothering with the others. It was noticed the following year when the ponies were brought to the surface again, the first one of the two friends to enter the field went in search of the other, and, not finding it, waited at the gate till the other arrived, and away they went again. This occurred every holiday and was the only time they ever met as the shafts were isolated from each other.

Recreational uses

The community could also, with the owner's consent, make use of the ponies in a number of recreational ways while they were above ground, and most of these uses certainly added to the variety of the horses experience. The fact that

44 The ponies from Waterhouses drift mine. This photograph from the 1920s may have been taken during a strike, but drift mine ponies were usually stabled above ground, often in the pit village. Such blatant riding of the horses, though, would normally have been frowned upon.

many of the horses were small, quiet and obedient made them very suitable as riding ponies, and those which had been 'backed' i.e. taught to accept a rider, were in great demand to give 'pony rides' to the children at galas, fetes and flowershows held during the holiday period in the mining areas all over the country. Indeed, there is evidence of ponies being brought to the surface at other times, specifically to perform this function. In similar circumstances ponies were also harnessed to light carts and traps, again for the pleasure of the local children. At some shows in the North East, before the Second World War, it was traditional for collieries to enter decorated carts representing the individual mines and these would be pulled by pit ponies, spruced up and be-ribbonned.

The idea of using work horses from the mines for riding was not new. At the wedding of pitman William Weatherburn and Elizabeth Oswald in Newcastle in 1754 the 'poor little coal horses' were released from their wains (carts) to take part in the pageantry,

the guests being mostly mounted double, or a man and a woman upon a horse, made a very grotesque appearance in their parade through the streets. The women and the horses were covered in ribbons.

A much stranger event is described in the following tale from a Notts./Derbyshire border miner:

I recall a fete and gala being held on Heanor Town ground in the very early thirties, when two of the larger ponies from Bailey Brook pit were brought there for a trial of strength with a certain 'strong man'. He stood in the middle of the field, like some well-muscled Tarzan, with arms flexed and legs akimbo whilst chains were attached to broad leather bands just above the elbows. One pony was Spanker, a large, mule-like creature who was very quick-cottered, whilst the other was a far more sedate animal, strong, but a slow mover. The affair was a fiasco! They simply couldn't get the animals to pull in unison, so the poor fellow was pulled hither and yon all over the field, to the great amusement of the mining fraternity gathered there.

45 An 'in-hand' pit pony class being judged at a local show. Competition was keen and ponies were brought in from all the surrounding collieries.

The showing of pit ponies

At events ranging from the local village Flower Show to the Royal Show and the International Horse Show at Olympia pit ponies have been exhibited and judged for possibly a hundred years. The already-quoted hoof-plaque from Kimblesworth told of Swallow's triumph in 1896, '*when 25 years old, he took 3rd prize among 20 other pit ponies shown in Durham*' and even now, in the 1980s the Moor Green Show, near Nottingham, one of the country's largest livestock shows, still holds classes for genuine retired pit ponies – their credentials must be shown on entry – and the winner represents his kind in the 'Personality Parade' at the Horse of the Year Show. At the Badger Box public house, too, in the village of Annesley, there is still an annual show solely for retired pit ponies, and, in keeping with these days of sponsorship, this local event has obtained the patronage of industry to keep it going. Moor Green held its last class for working ponies in 1970 and, obviously, even classes for retired animals cannot last much longer. Many horsekeepers, though, can look back on the first half of this century, when every agricultural show in mining areas held its pit pony classes and they were very well supported by the local collieries, between which there was great rivalry. At the Annual Horse and Sheepdog Show at Cannock Chase, for example, all the surrounding collieries entered two ponies each, and at Willington Flower Show, in County Durham,

they used to have the pit pony parade. They were in classes, ten hands up to, maybe, twelve. All the different collieries, competing against each other; there'd be over a hundred ponies here, from different places, Hordern and right the way round. Come from all over the place, the pit ponies.

The ponies were not only exhibited at local level. In 1931, for instance, the International Horse Show at Olympia featured a parade of sixty pit ponies from South Wales and Mon-

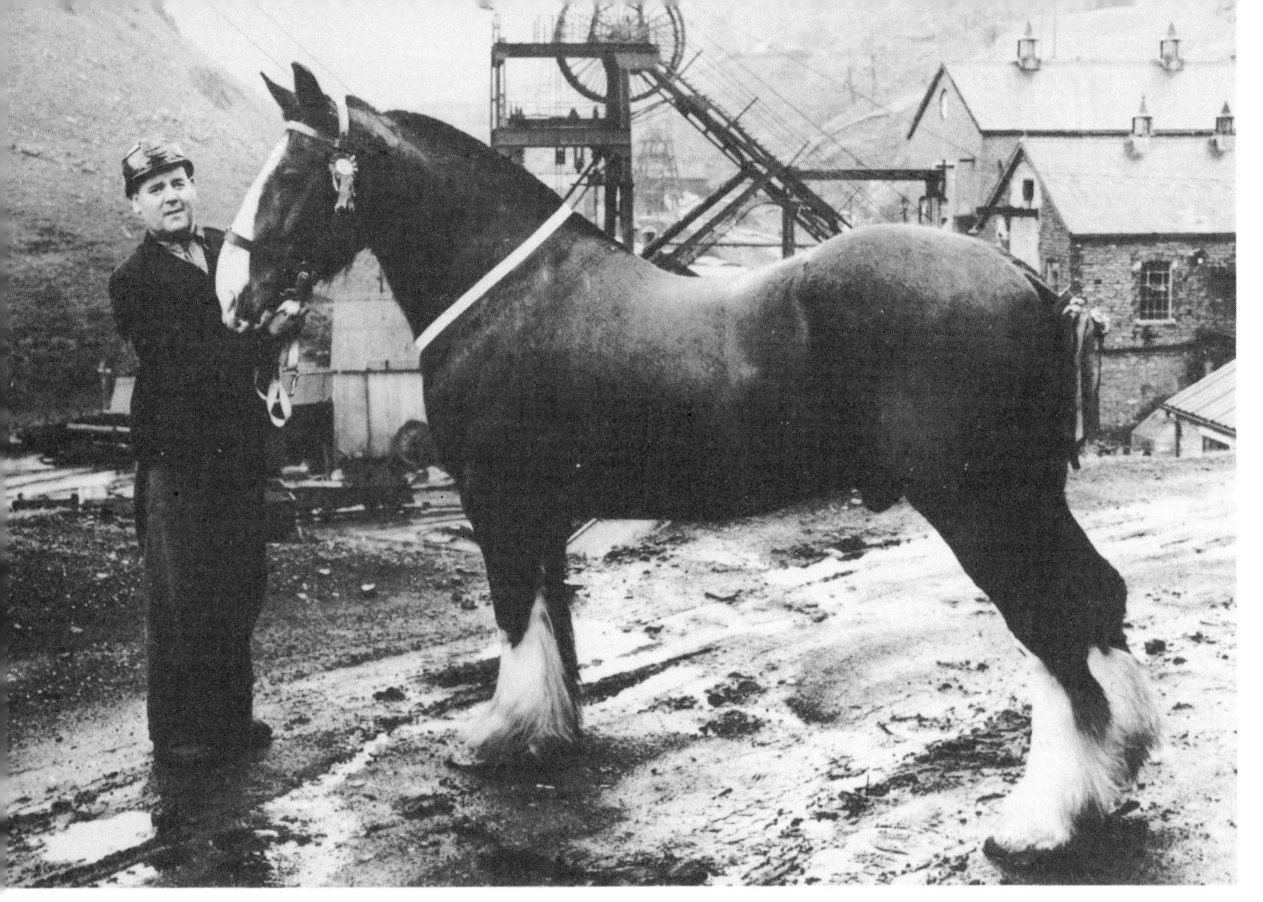

46 A prize-winning Welsh pony from Glyncorrwe Colliery in 1955.

mouth, with the ponies housed in stables built to represent the underground standings. The parade was led by 'Gwenny', twenty-six years old and the smallest in the parade, though 13.2 h.h. The preparations in Wales, and the intense interest in them, are recalled by a Welsh lady:

My father worked at Merthyr Vale Colliery. It was about fifty years ago, when there was a show of ponies at Olympia and he was chosen to take his pony on show. As children we were excited about it, as there was quite a lot of preparation to be done. We used to wait for him to bring it past our house for us to see. My father was very proud of him. The show was a success, I think, and my father used to tell stories about it, one being of Dame Laura Knight, the artist, going and painting the ponies in their stables and talking to the men. I believe it was the age of the pony and the number of years it had been underground which was the reason for it being chosen. Although a lot of things are very clear I'm afraid I am not sure of the name of the pony.

The rivalry between collieries, and even between coalfields, reached its peak at the Royal Show, which was held in a different place every year. Officially this was a non-competitive exhibition of underground horses. Mr B.G. Ackroyd, who was responsible for the organisation of the ponies at the Royal Show during the first twelve years of the NCB, recalls that

at the Royal Show we had an NCB stand exhibiting all the aspects of coal-mining and utilisation, and behind the pavilion we had the stables, usually a three-sided building so there was a grass area in the middle where the ponies each had a separate box and the horsekeepers had sleeping accomodation. Here the public were encouraged to walk along the lines of ponies and feed them tit-bits and talk to the horsekeepers. As far as I can remember we used to have six ponies each from Northumberland, Durham, the East Midlands, the West Midlands, Yorkshire and South Wales, a total of thirty-six.

Each day there would be a parade of pit ponies in the ring and at the final line-up the President of the Show would usually come down into the ring and meet the men and their charges,

(An exception to this general pattern occurred in 1953 when the Royal Show was held at Newcastle and over 90 collieries were represented.)

That the non-competitiveness of the Show was only a facade as far as the men were concerned becomes very obvious as soon as one of the horsekeepers involved starts to speak. The Royal Show, it must be realised, was perhaps the only occasion upon which horse-men from the different coalfields actually met together with the opportunity and the leisure to make comparisons. Consequently critical judgment was passed on every aspect of the other delegations. The horses, naturally, came under scrutiny, but so did behaviour, appearance and travel arrangements! In some cases there was little love lost between the coalfields. Witness a Midlander, a horsekeeper, on the subject of the North Eastern miners – his observations being based solely on experiences at the Royal Show:

They used to bring them tiny little ponies from the North East. Well, what good were they? They wasn't big enough to pull more than a man. We used to go to shows in a proper horsebox, three of us at the front with the driver, and four hosses in the back, an enormous thing. We hired it, we didn't have a box of our own. The Durham lot, they used to come in damned old lorries; we always seemed to be in front of that area, we always got a good van. We used to mek gam on 'em, them Durham men; they'd no more idea of keeping tidy than flying in the air.

The horsekeepers certainly enjoyed their week at the Royal; they were busy and 'on show' most of the time, but it was a paid break from the routine of the colliery, and as such it was welcome.

The early shows doubtless arose as a result of inter-colliery rivalry but later, and particularly during the 1950s and 1960s the showing of the ponies may be seen as half information service and half defensive action on the part of the NCB. It enabled the public to see for themselves that the ponies were fit and well looked-after.

In the competitive classes in the local shows the judges, often veterinary surgeons familiar with pit ponies, were looking for signs of the animals' capability to do pit work. Solidity, stiff and limited action which would conserve energy, and straight shoulders, were at a premium. These, and the over-all condition, rather than the conformation, were important. Usually the ponies were judged 'in hand', wearing only a halter or bridle, but sometimes they would be in full pit gear, in which case the harness also came under scrutiny. In some areas classes to find the cleanest pony were not uncommon, with white ponies often being exhibited. These animals were so carefully presented that the judges were known to resort to a white handkerchief wiped inside the ponies' ears and sheath, in order to come to a decision. The modern classes for retired pit ponies are judged almost solely on turnout, general appearance and appearance of well-being, thus giving opportunities of winning to animals which still bear the scars of a life underground and are not 'pretty' show-type ponies.

Horsekeepers, public and judges may have enjoyed the shows, but to present a complete picture it must be said that many of the miners found the whole notion of pit pony shows distastful. Their bitterness seems to stem from two sources. One was what they saw as the deceitfulness of the whole business:

It's all a big con. The public sees the show ponies and thinks that all ponies are like that, and they're not. They don't put the other poor wretches in the shows, nor their pictures in the papers; if they did there'd be a public outcry.

The other source of distaste lay in the unearned glory in which, in the days of the coal companies, the owners of the pit ponies basked, and the feeling that the shows were just another facet of the coal-owners' exploitation of man and beast:

The coal owner lived near the site of the local show,'

47 Pit pony classes sometimes required the pony to be in full pit gear, with a tub, and driven by a pit-lad. Here is a team, spruced up and ready, posing with the Horsekeeper who has also dressed up for the occasion.

wrote one miner, *and so was able for once a year, to behold the livestock that made him a fortune.*

The extent to which the owners and managers were prepared to lessen that fortune to pay for the keep of an idle show pony differed considerably from pit to pit. Some horsekeepers were fortunate:

At the beginning of the season, if you had a useful pony, the manager at our pit would let you take him out, and he'd never go back into the pit till the finish of the show season. You couldn't very well have them out for a week, then put them back, and then get them out at the weekend again, because they'd be up to the neck in filth, coal-dust and what-not. When they came out in spring they were out for the summer, till the finish, then back in.

To be shown successfully the ponies needed the hardness of muscle which a winter's work would give, but the horsekeepers also wanted to protect their charges from injury: '*They were supposed to work all the while, but you kept 'em off going up the road for a month before going to a show. You had to get him polished up and you didn't want him going lame just before the show.*' Those few weeks before the show could also prove difficult for the drivers: '*They were frightened to death to take out Tommy, the show pony. They'd say "I'm not taking him out", in case anything happened to him, it'd be more than your job was worth, so they'd take out anything bar Tommy. He was lovely; he was a "pit pony", he was down the pit, but ...*' Rules, even in the showing of pit ponies, could obviously be bent!

Many collieries would seem to have allowed their show ponies to stop work only a week or even less before a show: '*About a week before the show I'd get him up on top and there was a stable where you could go and look after him right and get him hardened up to the air.*' At Cannock Chase only three days' preparation was allowed in the

48 The First Prize-winner, Pit pony and Tub Class, Bishop Auckland Lifeboat Show, about 1910.

1920s which left the horsekeeper with a difficult task.

The standard of turnout was, by all accounts, impressively high, for many of the head horse-keepers particularly were proud professionals, jealous of their abilities and their reputations amongst their fellow horse-men. As showpieces for the mining world the pit pony shows and classes can only, on balance, have done the industry good. The rest of the pony workforce, the unshown and unsung members, may also have benefitted from the showing, if only through the public interest that the shows created.

The racing of pit ponies

When the ponies were up in the fields and being visited by their drivers it is a reasonable assumption that the lads would try to ride them, and, having succeeded, would attempt to race each other round the field. There is plenty of evidence that this chain of events was common in all the coalfields and that, at various times in various places, there were attempts to put this racing onto a more organised footing. The long strikes, particularly, gave opportunity for these occasions:

During holidays and the 1926 strike the entire stable was cleared out and the ponies set free in nearby fields. I also remember that several of us boys used to 'capture' our favourite pony and race them quite frequently, and the authorities 'shewed a blind eye'.

In Derbyshire

when the 1926 strike was on and the ponies had been up in the fields for a while, they used to have races. Organise them among themselves, they did, the gangers did, with somebody looking after them. They used to get racing, but I was a horsekeeper, so I used to keep well away. I wanted nowt to do with it.

The informal racing seems to have been very light-hearted, though when it became incorporated into more formal occasions the reason behind it was often serious enough: '*There were various events to raise money for the strikers at*

BOWBURN COLLIERY RACES.

WEDNESDAY, JUNE 8th, 1921.

Open to the County of Durham for Pit Ponies that have worked in the Mine for at least three months prior to March 31st, 1921.
To be ridden by Pit Lads, Bare Back, with Pit Bridles and Reins.

Judges:—IVOR L. JOHNSON, Esq., M. R. KIRBY, Esq. and P. HARLE, Esq.

Starters:—Messrs. F. G. LEIGH & J. G. RAMSAY.

Stewards:—Messrs. Chapman, Elliott, Sweeting, Barkhouse, Chitty, Hepple, Galley & R. Ramsay.

Committee.—Messrs. Wilkinson, R. Willey, Clowes, Fairley, Moore, Haddock, Owens, Lockey, Jackson, Elliott, Brown, Waugh, Carling. G. Lynn, Broughton, Coates, Harrison, Fawcett, J. Willey, Freeman, Bainbridge, M. Lynn, Hughes, Dunn, Mitchell, and Cowings.

Official Measurer—Mr. J. W. EDWARDS.

Official Number Caller:—F. OWENS.

Handicapper & Clerk of the Course:—W. F. GARDNER.

FIRST RACE 2 P.M.

All Ponies to be measured on the Field. Start 12 yards per inch.

ADMISSION TO COURSE BY VOLUNTARY SUBSCRIPTION.

BOOKMAKERS' TOLL 2/6. RACE CARDS 3d.

PROCEEDS FOR DURHAM COUNTY HOSPITAL.

Printed at the "Advertiser" Office, Saddler Street, Durham.

49

 Programme of Events. 

1st Race. TRIAL PLATE. First £1 10s.; Second 15s.

No.	Pony.	Height as per Entry.	Colliery.	Jockey.	Colours.	Result.
1	Sammy	11-2	Thrislington	— Frits	Light Blue	
2	Jolly	11-0	Browney	W. Wilkinson	Blue	
3	Star	10-3	South Brancepeth	J. Wood	Red	
4	Swift	11-0	Mainsforth	— Johnson		
5	Jerry	11-0	Bowburn	J. Allan	Green & Gold	
6	*		St. Helens			
7	Dusty		Bearpark	J. Farrey	Red & White	
8	Fiddler	11-2	Tursdale	— Denny		
9	*		Craghead			

2nd Race. CROWTREES WELTER. First £1 10s.; Second 15s.

No.	Pony.	Height as per Entry.	Colliery.	Jockey.	Colours.	Result.
1	Pitman	11-3	Thrislington	— Shaw	Light Blue	
2	Punch	12-0	Browney	J. O'Donnell	Blue	
3	Haig	11-1	South Brancepeth	R. Hodgson	Red	
4	Mark	11-3	Mainsforth	— Finlay		
5	Sailor	11-2	Bowburn	W. Harker	Green & Gold	
6	*		St. Helens			
7	Sammy		Bearpark	F. Crooks	Red & While	
8	Don	11-2	Windlestone		Red, White B'd	
9	Paddy	12-1	Tursdale	— Allan		

3rd Race. PITMAN'S DERBY. First £1 10s.; Second 15s.

No.	Pony.	Height as per Entry.	Colliery.	Jockey.	Colours.	Result.
1	Micky	12-2	Thrislington	— Banks	Light Blue	
2	Kit	12-2	Browney	T. Wilkinson	Blue	
3	Con	12-2	South Brancepeth	J. Hodgson	Red	
4	Haigh	12-0	Mainsforth	— Crowl		
5	Major	12 2	Bowburn	G. Knox	Green & Gold	
6	*		St. Helens			
7	Jake	12-2	South Moor	C. Swailes	Green	
8	Piper		Bearpark	R. Crooks	Red & White	
9	Boxer	12-2	Tursdale	— Denny		

4th Race. STEWARDS' HANDICAP. First £1 10s.; Second 15s.

No.	Pony.	Height as per Entry.	Colliery.	Jockey.	Colours.	Result.
1	Bugler	12-2	Thrislington	— Chatton	Light Blue	
2	Benny	13-0	Browney	E. Wilkinson	Blue	
3	Duke	13-0	South Brancepeth	A. Taylor	Red	
4	Marshall	12-3	Mainsforth	— Catton		
5	Jimmy	13-0	Bowburn	T. Robinson	Green and Gold	
6	*		St. Helen's			
7	Samson	13-0	South Moor	C. Brown	Green	
8	Shot	12-3	Tursdale	— Williams		
9	*		Craghead			

* Entered by Telegram and not yet confirmed.

50

5th Race. DURHAM NURSERY. First £1 10s.; Second 15s.

No.	Pony.	Height as per Entry.	Colliery.	Jockey.	Colours.	Result.
1	Jeff	12·0	Thrislington	— Norris	Light Blue	
2	Dobbin	12·1	Browney	B. Smith	Blue	
3	Gen	12·1	South Brancepeth	S. Spark	Red	
4	Pimple	12·0	Mainsforth	— Allan		
5	Tip	11·3	Bowburn	P. Robinson	Green and Gold	
6	*		St. Helen's			
7	Billy	12·1	South Moor	T. Clennel	Green	
8	Randy		Bearpark	H. Crooks	Red and White	
9	Striker	12·2	Tursdale	— Scott		

6th Race. BOWBURN HANDICAP. First £1 10s.; Second 15s.

No.	Pony.	Height as per Entry.	Colliery.	Jockey.	Colours.	Result.
1	Hector	12·2	Thrislington	— Miller	Light Blue	
2	Lenny	12·2	Browney	R. Ross	Blue	
3	Sam	12·2	South Brancepeth	R. Spark	Red	
4	Peter	12·3	Mainsforth	— Longstaff		
5	Bobby	12·2	Bowburn	C. Lynn	Green and Gold	
6	*		St. Helen s			
7	Lofty	13·0	South Moor	T. Roe	Green	
8	Mousey	12·2	Tursdale	— Westgarth		
9	*		Craghead			

7th Race. CONSOLATION WELTER. First £1; Second 10s.; Third 5s.
For Ponies placed 3rd and 4th in Races 1, 2 and 3.

1
2
3
4
5
6

8th Race. PLODDERS' HANDICAP. First £1; Second 10s; Third 5s.
For Ponies placed 3rd and 4th in Races 4, 5 and 6.

1
2
3
4
5
6

9th Race. COUNTY CHAMPION STAKES. First £3; Second £1 10s.; Third £1. For the Winners of Races 1 to 6.

1
2
3
4
5
6

* Entered by Telegram and not yet confirmed.

51

different pits. At these events there would be some pony races, all bareback of course, and they caused a lot of fun.'

The strikes of 1921-2 and 1926 saw a great number of pit pony races to raise funds, and as the occasions became bigger they became better organised, and were run, in fact, like minor race-course meetings. *The Durham County Advertiser* for Friday, June 24th 1921, for example, contains the reports and results of two such meetings the previous Saturday: '*The pit pony races held at the Football Field, West Cornforth, on Saturday were well attended, good sport taking place, backers having the best of matters.*' A glance down the results shows winners at 10-1 and 8-1. The other meeting, '*the open pit pony meeting which was held on the Jubilee Ground at Willington*' was promoted by '*the officials and committee of the Willington and District Soup Kitchen.*'

The Willington results indicate how keenly the results were contested, and may reflect favourably on the handicapping system, for no winning margin was greater than two lengths and most were in the region of a neck or half a length.

A more detailed picture of these 1921 race meetings can be drawn from two held earlier that month, on Wednesday June 8th at Bowburn, and Wednesday June 15th at Coxhoe. These meetings both boasted a printed race-card and examples of both have fortunately survived. The Bowburn card clarifies the nature of the races: *Open to the county of Durham for Pit Ponies that have worked in the mine for at least three months prior to March 31st 1921. To be ridden by Pit Lads, Bare back, with Pit bridles and reins.'* Then follows a list of officials – Judges, Starters, Committee, Official Measurer, Number Caller and finally the Handicapper and Clerk of the Course.

The races were handicaps according to the height of the pony, the start being 10 yards per inch at Coxhoe and 12 yards per inch at Bowburn. The ponies ranged from 10.3 to 13 h.h. Nine collieries were represented in each race at Coxhoe, and seven at Bowburn. Six collieries competed at both events. Each colliery had its own distinctive 'racing colours'. At Coxhoe there were six preliminary races, with prizes of £1.10*s*. for first place and 15 shillings for second. Then followed a 'Consolation Welter' for ponies placed third and fourth in the first three races, and a 'Plodders Handicap' for the thirds and fourths of the second three races. The meeting then ended with the 'County Championship Stakes' with a first prize of £3, for the winners of the first six races. The Bowburn meeting had no Champion Stakes, but the seventh race was a 'Consolation Plate' for ponies placed third in the first six races, and the concluding event was for ponies which had finished fourth in the earlier races. The prizes at Bowburn were £1 for first and 10 shillings for second.

49, 50, 51 Three pages of the pit pony race-card for the Bowburn meeting in June, 1921. Race-meetings of this kind were frequent in the North East during the strikes.

Comparison of the entries in the two meetings shows a number of ponies competing for their collieries at both, and intriguing speculation is raised when one notices that most of these animals are entered as being a different height on each of the race days. 'Kit', for example, running for Browney Colliery, is down on one race card as measuring 12 h.h., but on the other card appears as 12.2 h.h. As one inch lower is worth a ten or twelve yard start it would appear to be as well that there was an official measurer on duty at each meeting!

The meetings were obviously popular diversons during the strike periods, providing both entertainment and funds for the miners. J. Lawson in his book on *Peter Lee*, published in 1936, comments, in connection with the 1921 strike,

'*To leave London with its flaming headlines at such times, and to arrive at Durham to find the whole village at a football match, or all roads leading to a great pony-racing event is an unforgettable experience.*'

9 Anecdotes and verses

Many people have contributed the information and opinions collected into this book. They have given, by letter and in conversation, the details needed to create a realistic picture of the life and work of horses in mines. Frequently they have illustrated the facts by telling stories – anecdotes from their own experience – and in so doing have, often unintentionally, given invaluable insights into the relationships that existed between the ponies and the men. Many of these tales have already been quoted but some of the rest can give a final reminder that, no matter how much is discovered of the factual details of the pit ponies' existence, we cannot fully understand their lives in the pits unless we are aware of the importance of the ponies and men as living beings working in enforced partnership. So this chapter is an anthology of some of those anecdotes and verses, as told or written by the contributors, in their own words, and chosen for their vividness of description, their humour or their insight, but above all for the light they throw upon the way the men and the ponies related to each other.

Extracts from letters and transcripts of discussions are presented anonymously, as in the rest of the book, but where complete stories and poems are quoted, the writer is acknowledged.

Pony idiosyncracies

Many miners mentioned peculiar habits of particular ponies they had known. Here are a few examples:

'Glitter was a mild-tempered animal who would work like the rest up until 9 o'clock in the morning and would then refuse to work until the haulier who was in charge of him gave him a piece of twist tobacco. After this he was all right again.'

'There was one called Mouse, he did not drink the water in your bottle but would eat the cork, and if he found your clothing he would chew off all the buttons. When you had to hook his limber to the tub he knew whether you had put your foot between the rails or the plates as they were called, and he would kick out and catch your leg.'

'Wallace used to wait until you were putting his harness on in his stall and he would feel about with his left foreleg until he got onto your toes. All he had to do then was to lean on you and you can imagine the yells that used to come from the stall! He caught quite a few of us like this.'

'Little Vane was one of those who counted the clank of the coupling chains, but he was in a Union of his own – he would pull only two tubs.'

'One instance was when I was pony-driving from the coal face to the top of the jinny. The youth controlling the jinny had hung his waistcoat up with his snap and watch in the pockets. The pony had nosed around until he got the scent of the snap, and in the finish had chomped the snap, the waistcoat and the pocket-watch, so there was neither snap or time left!'*

'We had one called Honesty, you know, there was what you call a bait-hole, was shot out of the side, there was a choppy-box in there. Now, the foreshift lads, if we went down about four o'clock, and the backshift lads came in about nine, they had to take our ponies while we got our baits, back of the choppy-box, you see ... you put your bottle on there, and if Honesty was there, he would have your bottle*

* *Snap (Midlands) and bait (North East) both mean a packed meal taken to work. Bait-stand (p.99) is the break in the shift for the food to be eaten.*

52 Ponies and holidays, a debatable topic.

and the cork out before you could say Jack Robinson. With his lips ... he'd lie down ... with his lips, and the cork was out ... he used to waste half of it, you know, drink as much as he could, like ... aye ... Honesty ... I'll not forget him ... a skewbald ...'

'Several of the ponies used to like a pinch of snuff ... you used to put a pinch on the back of your hand and give it to the pony and he used to curl his nostril up, just as if he was laughing, then sneeze.'

'He would pull 6 or 7 full tubs at once, he would get down on his knees to grip the ground and pull away, and without a word from me he would know when to stop pulling and he would cross out from the road as I unhooked his chain and the tubs would run on into the other tubs. This pony was very intelligent, and I thought a lot of him, that much that I had a tattoo of Bloom's head put on my right arm in 1931 and it's still there, a reminder of those great, hardworking little animals who would never give in or be beaten.'

'We used to have what we called a tummyak, to nail the rails down; we always carried it, but if you touched Reaper with it, he just used to sit down, like a dog, and you couldn't shift him.'

A miner is describing his first day underground as a boy:

'The time soon arrived for bait-stand, uncoupling Duke with the pony facing in-bye. I was called to the end of the flat where Dad, my deputy, was waiting with the other drivers and putters to enjoy our bait. Before I started on this, however, Dad asked me to produce the raw apple and to shout 'Duke' and to my amazement and delight an immediate rattle of chains, etc., was heard and with quite a canter Duke appeared to look for and get his*

daily apple. This was the most likely way to gain the confidence and support of this particular pony; needless to say, the 'apple a day' became a must.'

'I had my shilling on Friday. I used to buy a penny's worth of damaged apples and take them into work on the Saturday. Dai used to make his way to where I worked, for his Saturday treat.'

Humour

A number of stories were told with evident enjoyment of the humour to be found in some aspects of underground life. Some miners were quite sure that ponies had a sense of humour! Here is a selection of tales worth repeating.

'George Morris the smith was quite a joker, but he surpassed himself that afternoon, for who should walk into the stables but two Yanks in uniform, the first that we had ever seen. They were being shown round the mine, and were surprised to see the electric light and the clean stables. George gave them a bit of a talk and then told them that we had an ex-circus horse, and took them to see Juno, a dark chestnut with a golden mane and tail. He told them that Juno would answer questions by neighing, once for yes, twice for no. Well, you ought to have seen them Yanks, they swallowed it hook, line and sinker. Iv'e always hoped that they got home after the war and are telling this story. You see, Juno was ticklish!'

'This is about a horse called Eagle, who was put down the pit before he was ready, for the sake of the costs. The hauler who was put in charge of him could do nothing with him, or any other hauler in the pit. After about two weeks he broke away while being hitched to some full trams of coal, ran away from the coal-face and ran into a broken roof support and was killed. There was a management enquiry. My father represented the hauler. My father claimed that Eagle should not have been down the pit without being correctly broken in for the work of hauling trams of coal. He won the case, and so the hauler was not held responsible for the death of Eagle. The funny part of this story is that the hauler told his wife that the manager had blamed him and that he had to pay the cost of the horse – £25 to be deducted from his paypacket at two shillings and six pence a week. The hauler used then to write on the bottom of his pay-docket "Horse – 2/6d." So he had an extra five pints of beer each week, beer being sixpence a pint in those days. After about a year his wife found out the truth and gave him one hell of a belting.'

'His name was Piper. What a rebel, a rebel who employed passive resistance as his most formidable weapon. Piper was a stint pony, which meant pulling twenty empty tubs and the haulage rope in-bye for about three-quarters of a mile. The first two runs of tubs he would pull till his belly touched the floor and take the run of empties in-bye without a murmur. The third run of empties Piper pulled his favourite act. The driver would fasten his limbers onto the tube and shout "Come on, Piper". Piper would just cock his head on one side, look at the driver as if to say "You'll be lucky" and gently sink to his knees and lie down. Nothing on earth, or underneath for that matter, would shift Piper. He would lie there oblivious of anyone about him. The drivers got that used to him playing this stunt that they played the same game and sat down beside him. After a short period he would, with assistance, struggle to his feet and carry on until he felt the need for having another rest.'

'There was a pony called Tansey at Bowburn between about 1955 and 1960. He had to pass the collecting point where miners gathered at the end of the shift and his driver, George Hardwin, used to lift the pony and carry it to the stables, as a party-piece for the miners.'

'There was a period when another young chap and I had to start work an hour or two before the others on the shift started. We had to go a mile in-bye to the stables. We would collect six ponies and bring them out-bye to the new district. We would bring them out of the stables, set them on their way, and he and I would follow behind and chat and sometimes have a sing-song. Then when we got close to our destination one of us would go to the front with our first pony. Then, one morning, we found one missing. I went back to investigate and found him in the stable. This happened several days, and always it was the same pony missing.

Mick was his name and he was jet-black. So we had to keep our eyes open really wide and it happened that halfway out I spotted him in a man-hole, just waiting for us all to pass him, and then he'd make his way back to the stables.'

'We had one ... what did they call him ... Spider. He ran out-bye when the run was coming in and nobody knew except the lad that was driving him and he was too terrified to say anything. I was a Landon lad at the time and when it came in, it was in the first tub, and it was just curled up, like a dog. Just lying, like that! We couldn't understand it, and we couldn't get him out, because there was only that much above the tub, and on the top, so we took the tub, as soon as we got the chains off and t'other ones set away, we took the tub and took it up to the Landon and just tipped the tub over, and out he came, straight back into us, and not a thing the matter with him. How that happened I'll never know, 'cos the run was coming in and he was going out ... so how he jumped in there I'll never know, but it is a fact, 'cos I helped to tip him out. Remarkable!'

'I had Bumble a while, when I was a driver. When we first went to start on the shift and he was in the mood he used to get under a certain piece of head timber and rub his back on it, and he would not move from there until he was ready. The rule was that he had to be brought out last, but the drivers used to bring him out first, just out of mischief, and of course no-one could get past him, and there was only one way out of the stables.'

'One horse by the name of Smart would, given the chance, chase after any light he saw in the dark distance, so the driver kept him on a check-rein. At this time Deputies were little tin gods. They had the power to sack you, fine you, or lay their stick across your back. The Deputies were hated men. The drivers of Smart had a system to put the fear of God into some of the Deputies. Each day a Deputy would make his usual examination of the district, being at a certain place at a certain time, punctual as Big Ben. On the Main Roadway you could see a light flashing half a mile away. So the drivers who knew the time the Deputy's light would flash in the distance waited in the darkness with Smart held on the check-rein. When the lamp came into view Smart would be released. A little time would pass then he would spot the light in the distance and away he would go, snorting and galloping. The drivers roared with laughter because they knew the Deputy was running like hell till he could get behind a ventilation door!'

'Major was one for going for a walk back to the stables if he got the chance, but I had one ace up my sleeve to stop him wandering off. He had one weakness, he would not open ventilation doors as most ponies did. To keep him safe and to know where to find him I used to put him between two ventilation doors, which were about 15 to 20 yards apart. Although he wouldn't open the doors he would try to kick them down, and one day I left him, kicking the doors as usual. I knew he couldn't hurt the doors, they were sturdily built. About two hours later, when I came back, there was Major at the other door, belting away at it like mad. I went and calmed him down, but he had another kick at the door whilst I was holding him, and I thought at the time that was unusual. Then I heard a voice on the other side of the door – "Have you got hold of that bloody horse?" It was the Deputy. He said "I've been trying to get through that ... door for an hour, and every time I pushed it open that ... horse kicked it shut!"'

'I've seen Rosie stop dead when taking timber in for the face, and she would not move. You would go ahead and see a pool of water or a fall and you had never heard a thing and dead quiet it was. She knew danger before it happaned, no doubt of it. One night after the break I went to the face to find her and she passed me, coming out on the conveyor belt! She could not get past a fall so when the belt stopped, somehow she climbed on. I don't know how, she was a big pony.'

Accidents

A number of stories about accidents were used to illustrate Chapter VII; the three which follow deserved to be quoted at greater length and so have been saved for this section.

'Mostly both drivers and ponies could sense danger in a mine. Some natural signs warned of danger and

most warnings came from the instincts of the horse and driver. One afternoon I was driving Taffy down a gate on the bottom of a fault. Now I will explain, a gate or roadway at the bottom of a fault was treacherous as the stone would slip off the fault without any warning. I used to bring one tub at a time out of this gate, round a turn on a large junction, and out onto the Main Road. I used to walk behind the tub so that I could twist it round the turn. Now when we got to the junction, which was quite low, usually Taffy would steady up so that the tub would negotiate the turn and not get off the road. But this particular run he went like lightning round the turn and kept going like hell with me running after him and wondering what was the matter with him. Eventually Taffy reached the Main Road and stopped. I got up to him and he was sweating more than usual, and looked a bit wild-eyed. This wasn't the Taffy I knew, there was something wrong, but what? I talked to him and patted him and we had a rest, but he still seemed a bit edgy. I fastened him onto the empty tub and we set off on the return journey, which was about a mile in-bye. I was plodding down the gate with Taffy following me in semi-darkness and we were approaching the junction. Suddenly I stopped and looked, I couldn't believe my eyes. The whole raodway was blocked with rocks and stone. The whole junction had collapsed. Six girders had given way under the weight of the stones. It took a fortnight to remove the stone and re-timber the roadway and it was estimated that at least 50 tons of rock was in that heap. My question is, why did Taffy run for the first time under that junction, why was he sweating so profusely? Did he know the junction was ready to collapse? If anyone doubts the story I can give them, for what it is worth now, the exact location of this incident. It was at the junction of Old 11s Loader Gate and the Fault Airway at Welbeck Colliery.'

'On one particular day I had hitched Tim up to a string of empty tubs and climbed into the first one. Off went Tim and I was, I remember, singing a popular song of the time – "Maggie". "Yes, Ma". "Come right upstairs" – when Tim stopped and wouldn't budge farther though I shouted at him. Then I saw him turn round towards me and I sensed that something was wrong and Tim had sensed it. It was then I heard a sound I'd heard before, a runaway of tubs coming towards us. I scrambled out of the tub; I knew I could do nothing for Tim, the road was too narrow and I had only seconds to try and find a "manhole", where the side was cut away at intervals to provide a shelter for such an event. I couldn't find one and all I could do was to squeeze myself upright against the side wall as the runaway tubs roared past me, breaking the bottle of tea which was in a "poacher's pocket" on the inside of my waistcoat, and my oil-lamp was hit and extinguished, and then I heard the crash as the runaway tubs hit Tim and the empties he had been pulling, just a few yards away. I was scared stiff and for what seemed ages I couldn't move, then with the smell of the dust in my nose and hearing Tim groaning, I just sat down and cried, and was still there when I saw lights bobbing towards me and some miners had come to see what had happened. One took me farther away and the others cleared the rubble and got Tim out. They told me his "cobble stick" – that's the wooden cross piece that the chain pulling the tubs is attached to – had up-ended and taken the weight of the runaway train as it hit the pony and then the roof, and, apart from limping badly, and the shock, Tim seemed alright. It didn't take them long to clear the road and I recovered quickly, not realising just how lucky I had been. However, there was no work to be done by Tim and me that day and we made our way with one of the men back through the air-doors, Tim still limping. But, once through the doors he must have known he was heading back to the stables, and his limp disappeared, and all the way back he walked all right till he got to the stables, when he put on the limp again and I'm sure that it was to impress the man in charge of the stables. I believe Tim had a few days off to get over it, and I did the same.'

'Me and my mate were sent to pump water out. This meant that we took a barrel down a short roadway with a pony. We then had to fill the barrel with a hand pump, then we would hang the pony on and take the barrel out onto the Main Roadway and empty it. Where the water hole was, it was

about eight feet high to allow the pump to be raised over the barrel, and in-bye of this place was a continuation of the old roadway. This had been left to close naturally. This meant that it had not been maintained as it was obsolete, and it had taken on the shape of a bottle on its side. The horse, when taken off the barrel would normally stand in the side so that we could go by with the barrel and fill it. This particular day just as we took him off the barrel a piece of dirt fell from the roof and he ran forward. We stood back, but no more dirt fell. Meanwhile the pony had gone forward into the old roadway for about 20 yards, on his knees, and he was wedged in like a cork, completely filling the roadway. The question was how to rescue the pony and stop him wedging himself more tightly. The Deputy was informed and he sent six men, rippers, to get him out. First, one of them crawled down to the back of the pony, speaking quietly to him all the time, so that he wouldn't be scared and go down farther. The ripper then hooked a chain round the limbers or steel shafts. Once that was on two men at the waterhole held onto the chain, thus making sure that the pony could not go any further into the bottleneck. The men started to dig a trench about two feet deep at the back of the pony, who had accepted the situation and lay there, seemingly knowing that the men were going to try and get him out. When the trench was completed up to the pony's hindquarters another chain was fastened to the shafts. There were four of us on each chain and we began to pull the pony back into the trench. We eventually got him into the trench, but then we had to make sure that his legs were pointing in the right direction. With a lot of crawling and going full length at the side of the pony we managed to get his legs from under him and point them away from him. Then it was a matter of pulling damned hard for 20 yards. It took hours. Everyone was wet through with sweat as it was red-hot in those old workings and practically no ventilation. Eventually we got the pony back where he could stand up. It was some time before he could stand as he had been fast for over four hours. At last he struggled to his feet, and apart from the sweat and being frightened, he was O.K. This was good news to the men who had worked so hard to rescue him, and they couldn't make enough fuss of him. This was and is typical of the mines, no man or beast will ever be wanting if he needs help down the pits.'

Ill-tempered ponies

The next two descriptions are included to correct any false impression that may have been given that all pit ponies are gentle and good-natured beasts!

'The one that finally ended my pony-driving days was called Stewart, a black stallion. He was a bad-tempered animal and his ambition seemed to be to put as many pony-drivers in hospital as possible. You had to keep your wits about you all the time with him. He would kick or bite, whichever was easiest, and when you entered his stall he watched your lamp to see where you were and if you managed to pass his back legs successfully he would lean on you, trying to squeeze you against the wall of his stall, and the only answer to that was to try and bluff him by putting your lamp on the ground at his off-side rear, then quietly pass him on his near side to his head while he was still watching the light of the lamp. I didn't like him very much, because he also had the habit of stopping when the walls were too close to pass to get to him and the roof too low to climb over the tubs, and you had to shout and throw bits of coal to get him moving again. He had his day, however, for we were going along the main haulage road to the workings and I was holding his tail chain, when without warning he lashed out with both back legs and I was just near enough to be kicked in the stomach and I collapsed. Fortunately the main haulage ropes, which are driven by electric engines at the pit bottom, were at that moment not working, and when I recovered I made my way back to the stables. Stewart was already there ahead of me, and I was doctored and sent home by car and put to bed. I had nightmares for a few nights, but when I had recovered enough to go back to work I did other types of work, and my days as a pony driver were over. I had enjoyed it until the day I fell foul of Stewart.'

'Another moke I think of was named Fly. Before I would put his harness and blinkers on I would whistle a tune called the Keel Row and straight

away he would start with his forelegs and hop from one to the other, never once would he fail to do this little dance, he used to have an audience round his stall. But once he was taken in-bye to his place of work he was a different animal altogether, and dangerous, too. When he was being yoked in his limmers one had to take great care never to touch his hindlegs with the limmers. If his hindlegs got knocked he would cause merry hell and run and kick out at everything in sight. We lads had to run and scatter into any refuge hole handy. Only by waiting for some time and letting him cool down, and with a little titbit of bread or a black mint sweet could you lead him back to his work.'

Verses

The first, by an anonymous North-Eastern miner, is taken from **Of Mining Life and Aal its Ways**, by Ned Cowan. The other two examples of pony-inspired verses are more recent compositions.

And very soon Aa had to drive
A pony like the rest
And though Aa wasn't perfect
Aa always did my best.
Once Aa tried me hand at yokin'
To the limmers heed fost in,
Aa even hung him on the tubs
But he wadn't stir a pin.
And soon a canny man went by –
Oh, laddies, what's thoo done?
Hees heed is where hees tail should be!
And he laughed for very fun.
And though that's years and years ago
In life's gay busy hive
Aa nivver will forget the day
When fost Aa learned to drive.

Spark

When I was a pit-pony driver
Just a boy all alone in the dark
In the dirt and the damp, with a smokey oil-lamp
My one grain of comfort was Spark –
There was something about that wee pony
On which I could always depend
Like the bond between shepherd and sheepdog
Or cowboy and four-legged friend.
I remember the first time that my lamp went out
The darkness was blacker than night
I clung to Spark's tail, knowing he wouldn't fail
And he led me right back to the light.
When snap-time came round in my snap-tin I found
That I hadn't got roast beef or ham
Spark was such a pet, he ate out of my hand
And got half of my bread and jam.
At the end of the shift, I came out of the pit
To wash off the dirt and the grime
I hated to go, leaving Spark down below
He stayed underground all the time.
One thing I liked, when we came out on strike
The ponies were all brought out too
It was pit-pony Heaven, that colliery field
The only one they ever knew;
I shouted Spark's name, he came up to the gate
And looked at me through eyes rather dim
In his horsey way, he was trying to say
'It's lovely to be up here, Jim'.
When the strike ended they went down again
To that dreary existence of hard work and pain
Where there was no difference between days and nights
And no chance of going on strike for their rights
There are no ponies now, in this mechanised age
But I've often thought, going down in the cage
A machine never greets you with whinnies of joy
The way Spark greeted me when I was a pit-boy.

J.R. Green, Doncaster.

Billy – the pit pony

I'll tell you of a very strange character, who
If you work at Winterbank, is well known to you;
He's worked there a long time, year after year,
And braved many dangers, yet never known fear.
He started work early, when about three or four,
When most boys start school – or a little before.
As to teachers and lessons, he ne'er gave a thought
He's only learned ganging, that's all he's been taught.
He's ne'er filled a tub during his thirty years,
And he ain't joined a club, so he's not in arrears;
He won't answer back, for he doesn't use cheek,
In fact he's so quiet, he won't even speak.
He's worked all his life and ne'er saved a cent
Yet nothing would represent all that he's spent.

When 'Loose All' was knocked he'd stop with a jerk.
He knew without telling just when to cease work.
He'd worked very hard, with never a grumble,
Like Uriah Heep, he's so very humble.
He's deserving of praise, but doesn't want fame,
His name's simply 'Billy' – yet what's in a name?
He still remains single, he can't find a lass,
To live same as he does, on corn, chop and grass.
You'll guess what it is now, I havn't a doubt,
It's Billy the pit pony whom this is about.
He's been at South Normanton a score years or more,
And all the officials know he's true to the core.
Though his life's been all work, he's shown plenty of grit,
And now he's retired to a field near the pit.
In this way the South Normanton Colliery Co.,
Their gratitude to Billy the pit pony show;
No doubt when he dies they will bury him there,
And a tombstone will then old Billy's name bear.
G.H., South Normanton (contributed by J. Spencer).

53 An unusually idyllic pit pony scene – at the National Coal Board Horse Hospital at Tondu, Glamorgan.

Relationships

Finally, here are two extracts from very full accounts of working lives spent underground. In the first the miner is describing his first day as a boy underground; he is not working with the ponies.

'*When I first saw Briton he stood just inside the door, his flanks going in and out like bellows after the hard pull up to that door. His head hung low. What it was drew me to him I'll never know, but my safety lamp showed me every detail like it was daylight, but it was his eyes which seemed to say "Not you too". He wasn't much bigger or higher than a donkey, but the thing that kept me worrying was, is he black and white, or brown and white? One or the other. I'd seen Tom Mix on the films, with his horse, and Buck Jones with his honey-coloured horse, also on film, but here, out of the*

blue, or the blackness, was all of them rolled into one, in my eyes.
My dreams and thoughts are broken by the leading haulier's shout "Right, let them through". After they've gone, your own company again. But wait. You've got something else to fill your mind, you've got a mate or pal. Come on, use your brain, how to get closer to him, to understand each other. Throughout that first day that we met I racked my brain for some idea to come, and at last it did.'

The boy collected the kitchen scraps into a paper that night and took them with him to the pit the next day ...

'The time had arrived, they were coming to the doors, horses, ponies and hauliers. Come hell and high water I wasn't going to open that door; they'd have to stop, giving me time to go through, look for Briton with the titbits I'd brought him, to show him that I'd not forgotten him. When I removed the paper wrapping from the scraps his head lifted – this smell didn't belong to this rotten, stinking world in which we'd met.
Now I had the answer; for Briton each day there'd be something different; if there were no scraps at home I'd fill my pockets with grass from the hedgerows going to the mine. But wait. On going into the mine I found that Briton had been sent into some other district to work. There was an answer to this, at the end of our shift instead of going to the pit bottom I'd go the the stables – they were quite close – and wait for Briton to come into his stall. When he reached it he'd find me there waiting for him with his titbits, showing that I'd not let him down.'

Shortly afterwards the miners come out on strike, and it is apparent that the stoppage will be a long one ...

'Now for the life of me I couldn't tell you who among the powers that be decided that it was time that the horses and ponies were brought to the surface and let free in a great big field on the side of the mountain. I can never remember that field having anything in it but cows from the farm. It seemed to be waiting for something special, and that something special had arrived.
People talk of luck, some seek it with money, some hope and pray for it, but luck turned her smiles on me, because living next door to us was Mr Griff Roberts, who was head man in charge of the stables below ground. He has watched the friendship that existed between Briton and me, seeing me in the stables waiting, asking me if I didn't want to go home or had I done something wrong. One afternoon he put his head over the low wall between our houses and called my name and what he said was like music to my ears: How about meeting your little pal Briton in the morning between seven and eight o'clock and take him up to the big field? I just kept nodding my head, no sound would come from within me. I'd be there at the crack of dawn, just to see him in the daylight. Black and white or brown and white?
The next morning I was waiting with lots of time to spare. Oh, how it seemed to drag. Now below ground something was happening that I knew nothing about until told about afterwards; the horses and ponies are sent up in alphabetical order, so I just had to wait until the letter Bs and at last, there he was, in the cage, with his head towards a world he must have long forgotten. The man shouted out my name – Mr Roberts had told him on the telephone that no-one else but me was to have Briton. I took his leading rope in my hand and started out for the big field, I was talking as if I was out walking with a human being, like a fool I was asking Briton to look at that lovely blue sky and listen to the birds.'

The boy made daily visits to the pony, taking apples and one day, to his great delight, his mother accompanied him, to see 'his' pony. The story continues ...

'After a very long time the strike came to an end. I kept waiting for just one thing, knowing that it had to come one day, the knock on the front door. It did, there stood Mr Roberts; I can hear his words as if he had just said them to me as I write "Well, you were ready to take him away from the mine, will you be as ready in the morning to take him back?"
At the field next morning Briton looked a fixture. Life had been so good. As I walked toward him, calling his name and telling lies, this time there was no apple, this time my hand was behind my back with his halter in it. I kept repeating over and over to him, it's not my fault, someone else caused this.
After a couple of weeks back at work I was

informed that it was time again for another change in routine, start night work. That meant the hours from 10 p.m. till 7 a.m. in another part of the mine. I would lose all contact with Briton, because small ponies didn't work in these high seams to which I was being sent, and he'd be gone from the stables when I got there in the morning, being a day-shift pony.

One particular day I'd got up from bed in the late afternoon, sitting by the fireside enjoying a cup of tea, when there was a knock on the door. My mother went to see who it was and called that Mr Roberts wanted to see me. There he stood as big as ever. He said "Lew, your friend Briton is dead." Just like that. My eyes were on his, no sound, I couldn't speak. Mr Roberts kept talking but I couldn't hear him. Yes, I was crying, like some clown. The words followed one another, "He's dead, he's dead". My mother asked in a quiet way who was dead, and when I explained she shed a few tears, remember, she'd met Briton on that Sunday evening when I'd been so proud to bring him to the gate.

Knowing that Mr Roberts would have to write out the report in detail I thought that the first time I met him in our so-called gardens I would ask him to explain what really happened. One afternoon the chance came, and his story I'll never forget. Briton was pulling his usual dram of coal when suddenly he stopped, for no apparent reason. What happened next God only knows, because off shot Briton, out of control, just dashing straight ahead, drawing the dram behind him, until it jumped off the rails, bringing down the large timbers and rock on top of him. His Haulier said to Mr Roberts that the pony must have gone out of his head. Oh, no. Briton, I think he had something in his head at that moment; out there somewhere was a big field and fresh green grass.'

L.J. Thomas, Daffryn, Mountain Ash.

The second story is contributed by T.B. Winyard, of Fifeshire, and has been previously published in *Fife Herald News.*

'In the flickering light of our tallow lamps the giant and I considered Nora as she stood in her stall munching contentedly at her feed. As my new-found friend enumerated her crimes and described her malevolent character I found his accusations hard to believe, for the little bay mare was the picture of innocence, and her eye was devoid of all malice and vice as she turned her head to gaze inquisitively towards us. She was bewitched, said the giant, a contemptible creature in which he could see no saving grace. She was all that was bad, wayward and intractable, spiteful and maliciously evil, and not a day passed when her perverse practices did not cause havoc in the world of darkness in which she lived and worked.

Her harness, complete with swingle-tree and tail-chain, hung on a peg behind her stall. As Goliath completed his account of Nora's depravity he said abruptly, "Get her ready." As I sprang to obey I exulted in the knowledge that I knew all that was required in the art of harnessing and yoking a horse.

She made no move as I fastened collar and hames around her neck, and I patted her glossy back as I turned away to collect the rest of her harness. Screaming like a banshee to the agony of vicious teeth biting into the flesh of my back, I only half-heard and saw the giant as he came to my rescue, for never had I experienced such sickening, excruciating pain. Later, as he dabbed Lysol on my wound, the giant emphasised with many an asterisk that I must never cease to be on my guard with Nora, for, he ended soberly, "She is Satan's wife." By the time we had finished that first shift I had regained some of my confidence, for nothing untoward had occurred, but it was with a sigh of relief that, on returning to the stable, I unharnessed the mare and then went to feed her.

I had learned my lesson, so ere I turned away, I held the scoop as a shield against her wicked teeth. Without taking aim she planted her two hind feet fair and square onto my buttocks. Rubbing my injured parts as I waited in the pit bottom for the cage which would take me to the surface, I reflected sadly that I would need eyes at the back of my head if I were to escape injury at the mouth and feet of this wicked animal which I wished to befriend. Vowing that I would treat her with respect from that day on I also made up my mind to try and gain her trust. I had learned enough to know that,

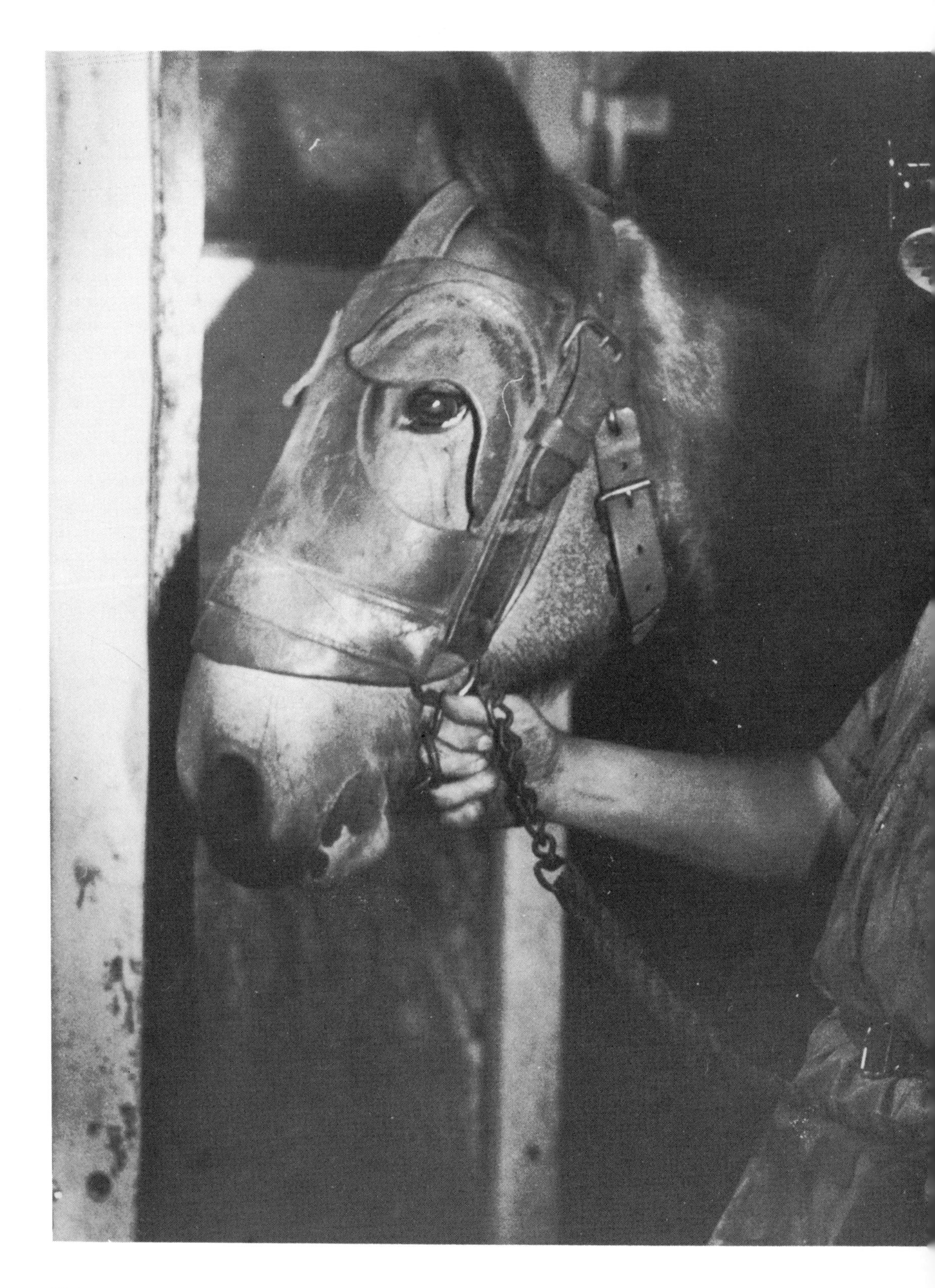

somewhere along the line, Nora had been cruelly ill-treated, and that her antagonism to humans stemmed from that experience.

It was not long ere I learned that she had two great loves, herself and her stable. Her tail-chain had to be tied with string to the hook on her swingle-tree, for a favourite pastime which gave Nora the greatest pleasure to indulge in, was to kick herself free of the chain, and then go like the wind to her stall which was a mile from where we worked.

Nora was completely unprincipled in the methods she resorted to in order to confuse and vex her oppressors, and, with a near-human intelligence, would change her tactics with diabolical cunning which had to be experienced to be believed. One day, when I had been lax enough to forget to tie her tail-chain, she broke loose and flew like the wind towards her stall. As I pushed open the heavy wooden door of the stable, which the mare could manipulate with an adroit shoulder, I entered and allowed it to slam shut with such force that the rush of air put out my light. Not unduly worried, I began to feel my way towards the stall by running a hand along the brick wall. Once there I knew that in a pocket of my jacket which hung on a nail was a box of matches.

In a stillness only gently broken by rats rustling in the hay and straw, I progressed in search of my equine tormentor. The manner of our meeting came near to being the last, and I ran into her hinquarters as she stood waiting, not in her stall, but three or four yards from it, blocking my path. Too late, I heard her squeal of demoniacal delight as she lashed out with lethal heels.

Later, as I retched and heaved in the arms of the giant, to the agony of my bruised body, he told me that, as he stumbled over my inert form, he had noticed that Nora moved a few paces from where I lay. She had, he explained, done this in order to catch him unawares, and thus deal with him as she had with me.

After a few months, when I was moved to another job, Nora and I parted company. At all times I had treated her as kindly as was possible under the circumstances of our acquaintanceship, yet I knew that I had failed miserably to gain her trust. Capricious as any fickle maid, she had led me on and used me abominably, yet I knew in my heart that I loved her.

Various levels, braes and dooks, led from the face to the pit bottom, and I often saw the little mare at work. When time permitted I would chat with her driver on the subject of her baseness of character, as she stood watching with eyes warily suspicious, for she was ever on her guard against human love and kindness.

One evening, having finished earlier than usual, I entered into the wide expanse of sidings which was the pit bottom. About a dozen men and boys stood amidst the havoc of a mass of entangled and derailed tubs, and it was with startled eyes that I saw what I knew to be the four tubs drawn there by Nora. A tub, or tubs, had broken away to run wild and with murderous frenzy to collide with the poor beast as she emerged from the level with her load. Cross-legged, Goliath sat cradling the head of the stricken animal in his lap. Tears ran unashamedly down his face as, in a strange crooning voice, he spoke the words of comfort which I hoped with all my heart that Nora understood. It was as if a mother, broken with grief, tried vainly to sooth her ailing child.

"Hush, noo, ma wee pet; hush, ma puir we beastie, it'll no be ower lang noo." Still crooning, the giant held the mangled head as the ostler applied the humane killer. Wiping away the tears with a bloody hand, my friend came to his feet, and I heard with superstitious awe the tirade that fell scathingly from his writhing lips. Cursing with solemn sincerity, he denounced and rejected the Deity who permitted his dumb creatures to live underground and to die violently. Glancing around at my companions I noticed that each stood cap in hand and bare-headed as if at a funeral. Furtively, I followed suit.

A moment or two of silence, and my hero spoke again. In a voice quietly reverent, he said earnestly "May the guid Lord forgie me me blasphemy."

He had said goodbye for all of us to a wee pownie which, because she had been ill-treated as a foal, had never known that love is instinctive and a force present in every human from birth to death. Nora had never known this love because her equine mind had rejected it, yet there is a chance that, ere she died in the arms of a man who had loved her, she had sensed its presence in her heart, and accepted its presence without question.'

Appendix I
The Clifton Colliery Horse Books

By good fortune a continuous set of three Horse Books of Clifton Colliery in Nottinghamshire survived when the colliery closed. They came into the possession of the Newstead pit, for eventual transference to the Mining Museum at Lount Hall, and through the interest of the Newstead NUM Branch secretary, Mr Brian Walker, the present writer was permitted to analyse their contents.

Individual books have been preserved at other collieries, but the Clifton books provide an unusually valuable source of information in that they contain a record of every horse that entered the colliery during an unbroken period of almost 50 years, 1874 to 1926. Unfortunately the histories of the individual animals are not all equally detailed; Book I begins with a list of 65 'Lives of Horses and Ponies, bought in the 10 years from 1874 to 1884' and gives only the name, when bought, when finished, and the years spent working with an indication of whether the horse's career came to an end by accident or 'worn out'. The rest of Book I and the other two books give a page to the history of each named and numbered horse, from No. 1, Whitefoot, a black horse purchased on 6 September 1876 for £50 from Meakin, to No. 492, Farmer, a brown 13.2 pony which cost £20 from Cope and went down the pit on 5 December 1926. The latest entry in Book III records the death in the stables of Dublin, No. 483, on 2 April 1941. Even so, the amount of information recorded is small for the final hundred or so horses – dates of entry to the colliery and date and reason for ceasing work is all that is given – but the first two books particularly are rich in a mass of detailed entries of every notable occurence in the life of each pony. By analysing these records it is possible to obtain a factual and reasonably objective view of some aspects of the lives of ponies in this specific pit during the period covered by the books. The following statistics, compiled from the Clifton Colliery Books, are included here as being of interest to the reader when related to appropriate sections of the text of this book:

Breeds

Specific breed names, e.g. Dartmoor, Fell, etc., are never given, but under 'Description' the following information occurs:
136 ponies are described as Russian (all purchased between November 1895 and June 1915)
1 pony is described as Icelandic
5 ponies are described as Welsh
102 ponies are described as English

Ages and length of service in colliery

The average number of years in the colliery, for all animals, is 8.33 years.
The average age of animals removed 'worn out' is 17.39 years.
The maximum age recorded is 27 years (this pony worked on the surface latterly, but 57 animals worked below ground until aged 20 or more. 3 ponies aged 26 are recorded).

Size

Of 470 animals whose size is given:
2 (0.42%) are 10 – 10.3 hands high
25 (5.32%) are 11 – 11.3 h.h.
100 (21.28%) are 12 – 12.3 h.h.
236 (50.21%) are 13 – 13.3 h.h.

No. 108 ~~Blossom~~ (18) Bought from Mr Thompson for £37.

Date	Age	Colour	Height	Description
31st Oct. 1894	5 years	Bay	15 hands 1½ ins	Horse

5 Nov 94 Taken down the pit
8/ " /94 Off work. Running at the nose. Makes a noise when working. Brought out of the pit
17th Nov 1894 Taken down the pit again
12th Dec. 1894 Off work. Lame in his near hind foot.
19th " 1894 Restarted work.
24th " 1894 Off work again through lameness.
27th " 1894 Restarted work
1st Jany 1895 Off work again from sprained foot as above
20th " 1895 Restarted work.
29th Jany 95 Off work. Had his shoe crossways on his near hind foot and getting a nail in.
11th Feb 1895 Restarted work
16/May/95 A slight wound on his top lip near nostril Not off work
13/Sept/95. Sprained his off fore heel Off work
16th " /95 Restarted work.
20/Dec/95 Off work. Sprained near side hock.
24/ " /95 Restarted work
14/Feb. 1896 Off work. Near fore knee swollen
17th Feb. 1896 Restarted work
11th Aug 1896 Killed in the pit. He was pulling 5 loaded trams down No. 14A main road but the lad (Henshaw) had neglected to put lockers in, the result being, that the trams ran into the horse, and in getting out of the way on the empty side his limmers got fast between two props. It is supposed he was strangled in this position. Carcase sold to Gillott for 20/-.

55 No. 108 from the Clifton Colliery Horse Register, Book 1. The two-year working life of a 15.1½ h.h. main road horse, with the details of his illnesses, injuries and death recorded in careful copper-plate handwriting.

36 (7.66%) are 14 – 14.3 h.h.
35 (7.45%) are 15 – 15.3 h.h.
4 (0.85%) are over 16 h.h.
NB 12 are simply described as 'horse' (i.e. 14.3 h.h. or more)
20 are simply described as 'pony' (i.e. 14.2 h.h. or less)

Illness and injury

Clifton Colliery Horse Book I records injuries and ailments of the ponies in greater detail than the other two books. Every entry in it is accompanied by the decision made concerning the seriousness of the condition – whether the pony was to stay in the stables (designated 'off work') or was to go for its shift as usual, (designated 'not off work').

The following analysis is of Book I entries only, for 184 horses for approximately 15 years up until about 1910, and relates only to conditions causing the ponies to be 'off work' for one or more days. There were 829 separate cases (though some entries related to recurrences of a previous condition). They were divided up as follows:

642 cases (77.44%)	Leg injuries and ailments. (These include 88 cases of wire or nails in the foot, 18 cases of shoe trouble and 42 cases of spavin.)
55 cases (6.63%)	Eye injuries
39 cases (4.70%)	Colic and digestive ailments
27 cases (3.26%)	Head injuries
22 cases (2.65%)	Influenza
19 cases (2.29%)	Soreness and chafing of harness
12 cases (1.45%)	Body injuries, cuts and grazes
13 (1.57%)	miscellaneous cases (e.g. skin diseases, blood poisoning, abscesses, etc.)

NB **1** The most frequent injuries sufficiently serious to be recorded, but not to prevent the pony from working, were injuries to the head.
2 15 cases of injury resulting from cruelty were reported.
3 It is worthy of note that there is not one specific example in this pit of 'rooving' – a pony injuring itself by banging its scalp or back on the roof, an extremely common injury in northern mines. Head injuries at Clifton tended to be on the side of the head, near the eyes.

Departure from the colliery, and death of ponies

The records of 458 animals (36 horses, 422 ponies) sent below ground during the period covered by the three Clifton Books give sufficient information for the following analysis to be made:

Of 458 animals entering the mine –

161 (35.1%)	were worked until classified 'worn out' and sold to the knackerman, dead or alive, at carcase rate.
132 (28.8%)	were re-sold as unsuitable, unmanageable, or prevented by physical condition from coping with pit work.
89 (19.4%)	died as a result of accidents. Of these: 55 were killed outright, as follows – 19 died from bolting and colliding with doors, girders, etc. 11 died in accidents involving trams. 4 died in roof falls. 4 were electrocuted. 17 died in miscellaneous accidents.
31 (6.7%)	were destroyed when lameness, etc., was pronounced uncurable.
30 (6.5%)	died below ground of illness, rupture, etc.
15 (3.3%)	were withdrawn from the pit because of blindness.
14 (3.1%)	died at the surface of illness, rupture, etc.

Appendix II
The Law and Pit Ponies

Appendix 2: The law and pit ponies

It was not until The Coal Mines Regulations Act of 1887 that any legislation provided protection for the horses underground. In it Inspectors were granted the powers to examine and enquire into, amongst other things, 'the care and treatment of the horses and other animals used in the mine'. The Act also required that roadways used by horses should be sufficiently high to allow them to pass along 'without rubbing against the roof or timbering'. These may not seem to be very great concessions, but it was a start and, in any case, these 'pony welfare' clauses have to be seen in the context of an Act which was also banning the employment under-

Horse-keeper's Daily Report on Horses under his Care M. & Q. Form No. 26

(Regulation 10(2)(a), (b) and (c))

Date .... Name or situation of stables ....

Name or number of horse	If taken from stables, time taken out	Name of every person taking charge of the horse (other than horse-keeper)	Signature of horse-keeper relating to columns (2) and (3)	Time horse re-turned to stables	Name of every person taking charge of the horse (other than horse-keeper) if different to column (3)	Condition (if taken from stables, on return thereto)	Signature of horse-keeper, relating to columns (5) to (7)	Pu if w mo 8 h th
(1)	(2)	(3)	(4)	(5)	(6)	(7)	(8)	

Signature of manager or person appointed under Section 10 of the Act to read these reports on his behalf .... Date........

Signature of under-manager or person appointed under Regulation 6A of the Coal and Other Mines (Managers and Officials) Regulations, 1956 as varied by the Coal and Other Mines (Managers and Officials) (Variation) Regulations, 1961, to read these reports on his behalf .... Date........

**Enter details in M. & Q. Form No. 265A.*

ground of girls and boys under 12 years old (unless already employed!) and limiting the working hours of the 12-year-olds to 6 days a week and 10 hours a day.

The major milestone on the road to a better deal for the horses came in 1911, when the Coal Mines Act included a Third Schedule on The Care and Treatment of Animals (Sections 86 and 109) and this became popularly known as 'The Pit Ponies' Charter'. For the first time specific instructions were given and requirements laid down, and the following summary of the appropriate sections of the Act gives an indication of its potential for improving the conditions under which the ponies lived and worked.

According to the Act no horse could be taken underground until it was 4 years old, and then only after a test for glanders, taken by a vet. The horses were to be properly housed in roomy, well ventilated stalls which were to be cleaned daily and, if not painted or tiled, were to be whitewashed every three months. No blind horses were to be kept underground. Competent horse-keepers were to be appointed, one to every fifteen horses, to ensure that the horses' condition was checked daily and the animals properly groomed and cleaned. Adequate food and clean water was always to be available in the stables and the workings, along with sufficient suitable

56, 57 M & Q (Mines and Quarries) Forms Nos. 265 and 265D; examples of forms designed to safeguard the welfare of pit ponies by ensuring regular checking of health and condition.

Reports of Examinations by Veterinary Surgeon

(Regulation 4(2) and (5))

M. & Q. Form No. 265D

me or number of horse	Report of examination	*Initial appropriate column			Manner in which any horse certified under Columns (4) and (5) was disposed of *(Regulation 4(5))*	Signature of person appointed to take the action recorded in Column (6) *(Regulation 4(5))*
		Fit for work below ground	Fit only for work above ground	Permanently unfit for any work		
(1)	(2)	(3)	(4)	(5)	(6)	(7)

* *Do not take into account temporary unfitness (which should be mentioned in Column (2))*

gnature of Veterinary Surgeon............ Date............

nature of manager or person appointed under Section 10
the Act to read these reports on his behalf............ Date............

58 End of the shift. One of the last generation of pit ponies on his way to his stable 'at bank', Sacriston, 1978.

medicines and 'appliances for the destruction of horses'. Proper daily records were to be kept of every horse, specifying its driver, its time out to work and back and its condition on return. Horses were not to be allowed to work if unfit, injured, improperly shod or wearing ill-fitting harness. All such circumstances, along with any evidence of ill-treatment, were to be reported to the manager or under-manager, who was required to 'exercise personal supervision' to ensure that the provisions of the act were observed. Managers also had the responsibility of providing an annual statement of the number of horses in the mine, the number that had died from accident or disease and the number of cases of injury and ill-treatment. Special Inspectors were to be appointed by the Secretary of State to examine the care and treatment of horses and to enforce the Act, assisted if they wished, by a qualified vet.

The proposals of 1911 were amended in 1949 and again in 1956, when the Coal and Other Mines (Horses) Regulations contained three notable additions. Management were now required to have each horse examined at least once a year by a qualified vet, whose examination report was to be kept for inspection. The period the ponies could be away from the stables working was restricted to not more than 2 shifts in 24 hours, not more than 3 shifts in 48 hours, and not more than 7 shifts in 7 days. The third important amendment controlled the disposal of horses declared unfit for work underground; these could only go away to immediate slaughter or to a home of rest for horses incapable of work, or to a responsible person who was not a horsedealer. Other new paragraphs made illegal the carrying of horses on vehicles, and any riding of horses underground, whilst in the stables the Act required the provision of at least one loose box to every 25 stalls, mangers and water-troughs in the stalls, and concrete or paved floors with suitable drainage, all in addition to the requirements of the Pit Ponies' Charter of 1911.

Index

Index of collieries and places mentioned

General Index